Introduction to
Chemical Engineering Problems

BUILDING THE LITERATURE OF A PROFESSION

Fifteen prominent chemical engineers first met in New York more than 30 years ago to plan a continuing literature for their rapidly growing profession. From industry came such pioneer practitioners as Leo H. Baekeland, Arthur D. Little, Charles L. Reese, John V. N. Dorr, M. C. Whitaker, and R. S. McBride. From the universities came such eminent educators as William H. Walker, Alfred H. White, D. D. Jackson, J. H. James, Warren K. Lewis, and Harry A. Curtis. H. C. Parmelee, then editor of *Chemical & Metallurgical Engineering*, served as chairman and was joined subsequently by S. D. Kirkpatrick as consulting editor.

After several meetings, this first Editorial Advisory Board submitted its report to the McGraw-Hill Book Company in September, 1925. In it were detailed specifications for a correlated series of more than a dozen texts and reference books which have since become the McGraw-Hill Series in Chemical Engineering.

Since its origin the Editorial Advisory Board has been benefited by the guidance and continuing interest of such other distinguished chemical engineers as Manson Benedict, Arthur W. Hixson, H. Fraser Johnstone, Webster N. Jones, Paul D. V. Manning, Albert E. Marshall, Charles M. A. Stine, Edward R. Weidlein, and Walter G. Whitman. No small measure of credit is due not only to the pioneering members of the original board but also to those engineering educators and industrialists who have succeeded them in the task of building a permanent literature for the chemical engineering profession.

THE SERIES

Introduction to

CHEMICAL
ENGINEERING
PROBLEMS

William H. Corcoran
William N. Lacey

PROFESSORS OF CHEMICAL ENGINEERING
CALIFORNIA INSTITUTE OF TECHNOLOGY

McGRAW-HILL BOOK COMPANY, INC.
1960   New York   Toronto   London

INTRODUCTION TO CHEMICAL ENGINEERING PROBLEMS

THE MAPLE PRESS COMPANY, YORK, PA.

Preface

This book has been written as an introduction to chemical engineering problems to be used before the student undertakes the study of physical chemistry, industrial chemistry, and industrial stoichiometry. Its goal is to help the student to attain a basic understanding of certain chemical engineering principles and to use that understanding in setting up and solving problems concerned with these principles. By means of discussion of a few important processes for inorganic chemicals, an effort is made to inculcate in the student the type of thinking that is necessary in process development.

Even though the book is intended for use before physical chemistry is encountered, various principles of physical chemistry are employed in it. These principles follow, however, as a logical consequence of the student's previous experience in basic courses in chemistry and physics. The concept of internal energy is explained and is emphasized as the basic element in the treatment of many chemical engineering problems. From the discussion of internal energy it is possible to proceed to the definition of enthalpy and its use.

Although concepts of chemical equilibria are presented, the derivation of the relationship between the standard free-energy change and the thermodynamic equilibrium constant is left for a more advanced text. The logical use of tables of thermodynamic data for computing equilibrium relationships is nevertheless allowed.

Because chemical kinetics is still an empirical subject, an introductory discussion does not require so much background in physical chemistry as one on chemical equilibrium would require. With that thought in mind and in consideration of the importance of chemical rate problems to the chemical engineer, a chapter on introduction to chemical kinetics in both flow and nonflow systems is included.

A number of problems to illustrate the various principles presented appear at the end of the book. In general they are of the type that will require more than just the stereotyped application of equations for their solution. If the student successfully works these problems, he will have made a good start in the development of facility in chemical engineering computations.

In addition to the problems at the end of the book, the first nine chapters include several worked-out examples. The student will find these examples a help in better understanding the text and in solving the problems. It should be noted here that there is no intent just to develop problem solvers, but rather a strong desire to see that the student learns by active application of principles he has encountered.

Special thanks are expressed to the Fluor Corporation, Ltd. That company was helpful in supplying certain figures which are included in the text. Also appreciation is extended to all those who cooperated in granting permission for use of previously published material. Acknowledgment of those permissions is given at each appropriate place in the book. Finally, many thanks are given to Evelyn Anderson who patiently worked with the authors in the preparation of the manuscript.

William H. Corcoran
William N. Lacey

Contents

Symbols and Abbreviations

a	activity
A	constant in Arrhenius equation
(aq)	in aqueous solution
b	specific gas constant, $\mathbf{R}/M$
C	concentration
C_P	heat capacity at constant pressure
C_V	heat capacity at constant volume
e	base of natural logarithms; equivalents of electron
E	energy; internal energy; activation energy
ε	theoretical cell voltage
F	free energy; total flow rate
$\underline{F}$	force
$\mathfrak{F}$	number of coulombs per faraday
g	gravitational acceleration
g_c	conversion constant, 32.174 lb$_{\text{(mass system)}}$ ft/lb$_{\text{(force system)}}$ sec^2
g_s	standard gravitational acceleration, 32.174 ft/sec^2
(g)	gas phase
H	enthalpy, $E + PV$
k, k'	specific reaction-rate constants
K	equilibrium constant
(l)	liquid phase
L	length
m	weight
$\underline{m}$	mass
M	molecular weight
$\mathbf{n}$	number of moles
N	number of equivalents

xi

N   mole fraction
p partial pressure of a component
P pressure
Q energy added to a system thermally; heat
Q' heat for a flow system
r radius; cylindrical coordinate
r   molal rate of disappearance; molal rate of reaction per unit volume
R   universal gas constant
(s) solid phase
t temperature, °F or °C
T absolute temperature
u velocity
V volume
W energy removed from a system mechanically, work
W' work for a flow system
x   moles of component converted
Z compressibility factor, $PV/\mathbf{nR}T$

d differential operator
log   logarithm to the base 10; Briggs logarithm
ln   logarithm to the base e; natural logarithm
(A)   concentration of component A
[A]   activity of component A
γ activity coefficient
Δ finite increment
∂ partial differential operator
θ time
σ specific weight
ϕ cylindrical coordinate

Superscripts
°   at standard state
*   conversion factor

Subscripts
C based on concentration
f for formation
P based on pressure, at constant pressure
R for reactor
st   at standard state
t total
0   initial

1

Units

One of the primary functions of the scientist is to observe the behavior of matter and to communicate his findings to others in an orderly manner. These findings are used by the engineer in his search for ways and means of assisting mankind to carry on its activities more effectively and more easily. Sound progress results only when observations are made and transmitted on a quantitative basis. Understandable quantitative description of natural phenomena requires the use of known and accepted units of measurement.

A simple example can illustrate the arbitrary nature of these units of measurement. One of these units of measurement is *length*. In order to compare the lengths of a number of metal bars, the shortest one can be chosen as a standard. It happens to have about the length corresponding to the span of a man's hand, and so its length is designated as a "span." By using this standard as a "measuring stick" the number of spans of length of each of the other bars can be determined. The quantitative description of this length for the benefit of other observers is complicated, however, by the fact that there is no way of knowing precisely the length of the bar used as a standard by the original observer, unless it can be borrowed or a duplicate is available. If there are many investigators working in the field and each chooses his own standard, confusion and misunderstandings result. In order to avoid this difficulty it becomes desirable to set up certain *standards of measurement* and to obtain as much agreement as possible among scientists and engineers to adopt and use these standards.

Because of the complications in setting up and obtaining wide adoption of standards of measurement, it is desirable to limit the number of arbitrary standards to the minimum number of quantities which must be specified in order to cover all the various measurements needed in scientific and engineering activities. It has been possible to provide for all necessary measurements in terms of four arbitrarily chosen quantities, which are called *fundamental concepts*. It has not been possible, however, to obtain universal agreement among all the interested persons with respect to either the particular fundamental concepts chosen or the magnitudes of units representing them. Because this lack of agreement has persisted for a long time, several systems of units differing markedly from each other are in wide use. Each is so firmly established that it seems unlikely in the near future that any one system will achieve universal adoption, as desirable as this goal may be.

Systems of Units

As a result of this lack of agreement the engineer is called upon to be familiar with several systems of units and to work effectively in terms of each. Most measurements made in scientific laboratories use *metric units*, whereas most engineering work in English-speaking countries is carried on in the *English system of units*. Because the engineer must be able to utilize the results obtained by the scientist he must be conversant with both systems.

An added complication occurs within the English system in the choice of fundamental concepts. In the metric system the fundamental concepts ordinarily used are mass, length, time, and temperature, the corresponding units being grams, centimeters, seconds, and degrees centigrade, respectively, or multiples of them. In one English system the fundamental concepts, as above, are mass, length, time, and temperature, the units being pounds, feet, seconds, and degrees Fahrenheit. The other English system is based upon force, length, time, and temperature with pounds, feet, seconds, and degrees Fahrenheit as units. These systems can be interrelated through suitably established *conversion factors*. Each of the two English systems has certain advantages over the other, the primary difference between them being in the nature of the unit called a *pound*.

After a set of four fundamental concepts or fundamental

dimensions has been selected and given corresponding units, other quantities of engineering interest can be derived from them. The relation of a number of derived quantities expressed in terms of fundamental dimensions is shown in Table 1-1 for each of the three systems discussed above.

TABLE 1-1. UNITS AND DIMENSIONS

Quantity	Dimensions	Units		
		cgs metric system	English mass, or absolute system	English force, or gravitational system
Length	L	cm	ft	ft
Time	θ	sec	sec	sec
Temperature	T	°C	°F	°F
Mass	m or $F\theta^2/L$	g	lb	slug
Force	mL/θ^2 or F	dyne	poundal	lb
Area	L^2	cm²	ft²	ft²
Volume	L^3	cm³	ft³	ft³
Velocity	L/θ	cm/sec	ft/sec	ft/sec
Acceleration	L/θ^2	cm/sec²	ft/sec²	ft/sec²
Density	m/L^3 or $F\theta^2/L^4$	g/cm³	lb/ft³	slug/ft³
Specific weight	m/θ^2L^2 or F/L^3	dyne/cm³	poundal/ft³	lb/ft³
Specific volume	L^3/m or $L^4/F\theta^2$	cm³/g	ft³/lb	ft³/slug
Pressure	$m/L\theta^2$ or F/L^2	dyne/cm²	poundal/ft²	lb/ft²
Energy	mL^2/θ^2 or FL	erg	ft-poundal	ft-lb
Power	mL^2/θ^3 or FL/θ	erg/sec	ft-poundal/sec	ft-lb/sec
Heat capacity†	L^2/θ^2T	erg/(g)(°C)	ft-poundal/(lb)(°F)	ft-lb/(slug)(°F)

† Other more convenient units of heat capacity will be discussed later.

Mass is a measure of the quantity of material in a given sample, and the standards in both the metric and English mass systems are reference samples of metal which are carefully prepared and preserved. The standard of mass in the English mass system is used as the basis for definition of the standard unit of force in the English force system. A *force* of 1 pound in the force system is defined as the force exerted by the 1-pound-mass standard of the mass system in a standard gravitational field. This corresponds to the *weight* of the mass standard under conditions such that the gravitational acceleration has the value of 32.1740 ft/sec², which may be called g_s. Although the fundamental force unit in the force system is defined in terms of the fundamental mass unit of the mass system, the two quantities have different dimensions as shown in Table 1-1, and thus are not interchangeable quantities. If standard gravitational acceleration is assumed to apply at all times, however, weight may serve as an indirect but useful measure of quantity of material. For many purposes this assumption is sufficiently accurate to cover engineering situations. Gravitational acceleration varies with latitude and elevation above mean sea level, but the value changes by only about 0.5% from latitude 0 to 90°, and by 0.1% from sea level to an altitude of 10,000 ft. If greater accuracy is required, weights can be corrected to those for standard gravity, but for present purposes standard gravity will be assumed.

Because the engineer is much interested in forces and their effects on matter and because his measure of quantities of material is usually by weight, it is simpler and more convenient for him to use the English force system in his calculations. For example, he feels more at ease when he expresses pressure in pounds per square foot than in poundals per square foot, as he would have to in the English mass system. *In the discussions to follow, therefore, the English force-length-time-temperature system will be used with the assumption of standard gravitational acceleration.* The value of g_s will be designated as g, with a value of 32.174 ft/sec².

Engineers frequently use a constant g_c, which has the units lb(mass system) ft/lb(force system) sec², and the numerical value of 32.174. For example, a body is weighed with a spring scale at a location for which the gravitational acceleration g is 32.14 ft/sec², which would correspond approximately to the latitude of San Francisco and an elevation of 4000 ft above sea level. The spring scale measures force and in this case it registers m lb, in the force system. The mass of this object, in pounds in the mass system, will be $\underline{m} = m(g_c/g) = m(32.174/32.14) = 1.001\ m$ lb.

Conversely, if a mass of $\underline{m}$ lb (in the mass system) were to be weighed at the same location, its weight in terms of pounds (in the force system) would be

$$m = \underline{m}\frac{g}{g_c} = \underline{m}\frac{32.14}{32.174} = 0.999\ \underline{m}\ \text{lb}$$

If the weighing had taken place where the gravitational acceleration had its standard value, $g_s = 32.174$ ft/sec², the weight would have been $\underline{m}(32.174/32.174) = \underline{m}$ lb, in accordance with the definition of the pound in the force system.

Although the mass of a body is constant, regardless of the magnitude of the gravitational acceleration, its weight is affected by its location in the gravity field. It can be seen from the values found above that, for the purposes of most engineering calculations, the assumption that g/g_c is equal to unity or that $g = g_s$ = 32.174 ft/sec² does not involve a serious error. From the numerical value and the units for g_c given above it is evident that this assumption merely restates the definition of 1 lb in the force system as that force exerted upon a mass of 1 lb in the mass system in a gravitational field having the standard acceleration of 32.174 ft/sec².

Thermal Units

The foot-pound is not always a convenient unit of energy, and another unit has been independently defined as the *British thermal unit* or Btu. An exactly similar procedure was followed in the metric system, in which the erg and calorie are independently defined units of energy. The *Btu* may be defined† for present purposes as the energy required to raise the temperature of a mass of water (at the temperature for its maximum density) corresponding to 1 pound in the mass system by 1°F. As noted above, this mass has the same number of molecules as a weight of 1 pound in the system used here. The *foot-pound* is defined as the energy involved when a force of 1 pound acts through a distance of 1 foot. Its relation to the Btu can only be determined experimentally and would not be expected to be an even value. The accepted factor is subject to change as more accurate determinations are made. For present purposes 1 Btu will be taken as equivalent to 778.2 ft-lb. This value is commonly known as the "mechanical equivalent of heat." This conversion factor changes the units in which energy is expressed but does not affect the dimensions of it.

Conversion Factors

Some of the commonly used conversion factors are shown in Table 1-2 with sufficient accuracy for present use.

† The Btu has been redefined in terms of electrical units, and is 0.29321 watt-hour.

TABLE 1-2. CONVERSION FACTORS

Multiply	By	To obtain
in.	2.54	cm
cm^3	3.53 × 10^{-5}	ft^3
ft^3	7.48	gal
lb	453.6	g
g/cm^3	62.43	lb/ft^3
dynes/cm^2	1.450 × 10^{-5}	psi (lb/in.^{2})
psi	2.036	inches of mercury column at 32°F (in. Hg)
psi	27.7	in. H$_2$O (60°F)
atm	76.0	cm Hg (32°F)
atm	29.9	in. Hg (32°F)
atm	33.9	ft H$_2$O (60°F)
atm	14.7	psi
Temperature difference, °C	1.8	Temperature difference, °F
°K	1.8	°R
cal (gram-calories)	3.966 × 10^{-3}	Btu
cal/g	1.8	Btu/lb
cal/(g)(°C)	1	Btu/(lb)(°F)
Btu	778.2	ft-lb
hp	550	ft-lb/sec
hp-hr	2544	Btu
kw	0.948	Btu/sec
kw	1.341	hp
kw-hr	3412	Btu

Units Used in This Book

Engineering calculations are commonly made in terms of English force-length-time units but must be based frequently on data which are obtained and published in the metric mass-length-time system. It is necessary, therefore, to be able to use both systems and to be clear at any time as to which system is actually involved. In order to avoid confusion, it is desirable to establish certain conventions to be followed consistently throughout the present treatment.

All units involved in any single expression or equation will belong consistently to one system or the other, and will not be a mixture of systems. For example, in the equation,

$$C_P \, \Delta T + P \, \Delta V = 25.1 \text{ Btu/lb}$$

the unit given at the end indicates that the English system is involved. Then English units are concerned throughout, and C_P would be expressed† in Btu/(lb)(°R), T in degrees Rankine, P ordinarily in psia, V in ft³/lb. It is obvious from these units that a dimensional conversion factor must be used with the $P \, \Delta V$ term to make it consistent with and additive to the other terms. This factor would have the units of (Btu/lb)/(psi)(ft³/lb), which has the numerical value of 0.1850. If the final unit given in the equation above had been cal/g instead of Btu/lb, the other units involved would have been cal/(g)(°K), degrees Kelvin, atmospheres (ordinarily), and liters/g, respectively, with a conversion factor having the units of (cal/g)/(atm)(liters/g).

If on the other hand, the final unit had been Btu/mole, the other units would be Btu/(lb mole)(°R), degrees Rankine, psia, ft³/lb mole. Rather than stating in each case whether pound moles or gram moles are involved, the term mole will be used, and the distinction will follow from other units given in the same relation. For example, when feet or Btu and moles occur together, pound moles are involved, whereas, when centimeters or calories and moles are associated, gram moles are implied.

† Note that *heat capacity* is expressed here as energy per unit of weight per degree Rankine, whereas in Table 1-1 heat capacity is defined as energy per unit mass per degree Fahrenheit. The implied redefinition in terms of weight is compatible with the discussion on page 4 wherein it is stated that for engineering purposes weight may serve as an indirect but useful measure of quantity of material.

2

Engineering Calculations

The engineer makes his major contributions through the use of experimental facts and quantitative thinking to develop useful results. He must, therefore, understand the facts and their background and then be able to piece them together in such a way that he will obtain a dependable answer to the problem on which he is working. This means that he must exercise both ingenuity and care in the manipulation of the data which he has available. It frequently happens that he does not have all the information he wishes, and he realizes that he will not be able to get so precise a result as he could otherwise. Rather than to give up and obtain no useful result, he can often exercise his ingenuity and judgment by *estimating* values which may serve as a working approximation of the facts he needs. Such estimation is often based on use of knowledge available for similar materials and situations. The procedure undoubtedly brings some uncertainty into his final result, but in many situations engineering decisions can be satisfactorily based on somewhat uncertain results when it is clearly understood that the uncertainty exists.

A simple example may serve to illustrate this point. The superintendent of a chemical plant wishes to operate a piece of machinery in a different way from that for which it was designed and requests an engineer to specify the size of motor which should be installed. The engineer has no specific facts regarding the friction which will result from the new operation, but from experience with other equipment he believes that he can estimate the friction within 20% of its actual value. On this basis he

8

combines this estimated value with other known factors and calculates that 3.6 hp will be required. Because of the unavoidable uncertainty in this value he specifies a 5-hp motor. Thus he has obtained a useful result which helps the superintendent to avoid the possible error of installing a 2-hp motor, which would be too small, or a 10-hp motor which would be too large and costly. If the engineer had not recognized and allowed for the uncertainty in his calculations, his report might have caused difficulties for the superintendent.

Organization of Calculations

During his period of education the engineer should have the opportunity to practice and perfect the techniques of organizing engineering problems, analyzing the situations involved, finding ways of getting at the solution, gathering the necessary background of information, completing the necessary calculations, and preparing readily understandable reports which will communicate his ideas and results to others. Although time is not ordinarily available in one course for the preparation of many comprehensive engineering reports of this sort, the different elements of work going into such projects are met in various engineering courses. If the student realizes the over-all objective of his training and these exercises, he is likely to obtain from them the greatest benefit to his career. *The primary function of an engineering education is not so much transmission and absorption of even very useful facts as it is familiarization of the student with the fundamental methods of attack upon problems arising from new situations, and provision of sufficient opportunity to use them.* Their use develops confidence in meeting new and difficult engineering situations that continually arise in the practice of the profession.

Usually a number of steps and an assortment of different pieces of information must be included in an engineering calculation. As a result there are numerous opportunities for making errors in the course of such calculations. Because the engineer must be able to rely on his own computations and because his reputation is built upon his ability and his dependability, he must take great pains to avoid errors, as well as unnecessary uncertainties. Errors in computation are exceedingly easy to make, and in order to avoid or eliminate them careful work and the use of all available protective techniques are required.

Records of Calculations

In order that the report of a calculation may be understood it is essential that each step taken can be followed easily by the reader. If a report is to be accepted and put to use, it must be considered and appraised by other engineers. Unless the work can be quickly understood its chances for adoption are markedly decreased. Because it is not difficult to make the steps of a calculation clear, it is poor policy not to develop the habit of doing this as a matter of course. Not only will neat, clear work assist others in appreciating the results, but it will also repay the writer himself by making him think in an orderly manner and by making it much easier for him to go back over his own work critically. More time can be wasted by the writer trying to find out what he did a day or so before than he would have expended in expressing the work intelligibly in the first place. If the *writer* has difficulties of this sort, one can imagine that a person who had not already been through the steps would have many more such difficulties.

When a number of factors enter into a computation, their relationship can be simply stated by methods which are well known to all familiar with mathematics. Let us say, for example, that an aqueous solution having a specific weight of 69 lb/ft³ is flowing steadily through a pipe at an average velocity of 2 ft/sec, the pipe having an inside diameter of 2.1 in. It is desired to calculate the weight of solution passing through the pipe per hour. The computation can be expressed as follows:

$$\underset{\pi/4}{(0.7854)} \underset{\text{diam}^2}{\overset{*}{(2.1/12)^2}} \underset{\text{vel}}{(2)} \underset{\text{sec/hr}}{\overset{*}{(3600)}} \underset{\text{sp wt}}{(69)} = 11,950 \text{ or } \underset{\text{wt rate}}{12,000 \text{ lb/hr}}$$

Aside from $\pi/4$ and the two quantities labeled with asterisks to indicate that they are conversion factors, all figures shown come from the statement of the problem and can thus be easily identified. The first two parentheses can be seen to give the area of cross section of the pipe, and, when combined with the velocity, they give the volume of solution passing through the pipe per second. Multiplying this quantity by the number of seconds per hour gives the volumetric output per hour, and, when this is combined with the weight per unit volume, the result is the output in terms of lb/hr as desired. Although the calculation gives a final value of 11,950 lb/hr, the precision with which the data are given is not such as to encourage confidence in so many significant figures, and so the result is rounded off to 12,000 lb/hr.

Checking Calculations

Writing the expression in the form shown above has taken almost no extra time, and yet the statement can be used in a number of useful ways. A *check* can be made to see that all necessary factors have been included and that they are "right side up." Because a slide-rule error could have been made, the numerical work can be checked by starting at the other end of the series of terms to avoid following back through the original set of mechanical operations and thus making the same error twice, a thing which is very easy to do. Sometimes an independent check can be accomplished by using four-place logarithms to duplicate a slide-rule calculation. This method can also serve effectively to check decimal points.

Most of the quantities involved in the equation cited are dimensional, and a combination of the units of the individual terms should result in the units ascribed to the final result. This very useful "dimensional check" can be written as follows:

$$\text{(No dimension)} \left(\frac{\text{in.}}{\text{in./ft}}\right)^2 \left(\frac{\text{ft}}{\text{sec}}\right) \left(\frac{\text{sec}}{\text{hr}}\right) \left(\frac{\text{lb}}{\text{ft}^3}\right) = \frac{\text{lb}}{\text{hr}}$$

This type of checking will often reveal the omission of a necessary factor or an inconsistency in units used.

Another useful means of checking a calculation is to replace the factors involved by simple whole numbers of approximately the same magnitude in order to learn whether the result obtained in the primary calculation is of the right order of magnitude. This check will often call attention to errors in decimal points and to gross errors of slide-rule manipulation. Another procedure is to substitute suitable powers of ten for the factors in order to make a check upon the decimal point of the result. *One of the most useful tests of all, however, is that of reasonableness.* In this case the computer divorces himself from the details of the problem and asks himself whether the answer should be large or small, positive or negative, etc.; in other words, he considers whether or not the result he has obtained is in general what he would expect when viewing the physical picture involved. For example, if he were calculating the amount of friction occurring in a mechanical process and the result came out negative, he would sense that something was wrong and seek out the error.   Or in the example cited above, if the result found had been 12 lb/hr, he would realize that this is a very small amount of solution (less than a bucketful) to flow out of a 2-in. pipe in an hour's time. Although the test of reasonableness will not draw attention to small errors, it will point out the large ones which unfortunately often occur.

Time and energy are saved if a careful check is made after each step in a calculation.   If the logic and accuracy of each step must be justified before the next is undertaken, the necessity is avoided later for making corrections throughout a whole series of steps following the point where the error has occurred.   Step-by-step checking involves no more labor than going over the work after completion, and, because there seems to be more tendency to make careless errors near the start of a calculation, correcting them immediately not only is saving of time but also avoids chagrin.

Use of Calculus

In a large number of the situations he encounters the engineer is able to get great assistance from the use of very simple calculus. Whenever the situation is changing as the result of change of one or more controlling variables, the calculus offers an approach to the analysis of the operation.   For this reason it is important that the engineer become familiar with the application of this mathematical approach to the solution of physical problems.

If it is evident in a given operation that systematic changes are occurring with respect to time, temperature, or any other pertinent variable, and it is desired to know the over-all result of the operation during the period while these changes are taking place, the engineer knows that use of the calculus is indicated.   One or two simple illustrations may serve to show the general approach to these problems.

A curved-bottom tank, symmetrical about a vertical plane through the bottom point, has a flat end section shaped as shown in Fig. 2-1.   The bottom point may be taken as an origin of coordinates, and the horizontal half width of the section at any elevation called l.   The corresponding height of the point vertically above the origin may be called h, and the curve of the edge of the section expressed as a function of h and l can be ascertained by measurement. Let us say that in a given case it is found that the curve is described by the equation $h = 0.36l^2$, in which both h and l are in feet. It is desired to know what area of the end section is submerged when the tank is filled to a level 3 ft above the bottom point.

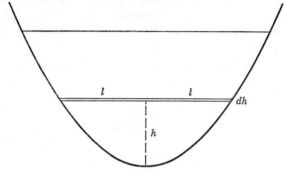

FIG. 2-1. End view of tank.

Because l is changing with respect to h, it is best to consider the area of a very small section of the whole area as shown in the figure. The value of l for this infinitesimal change in h may be taken as constant, and the area of the section is $2l \, dh$. The total area of the tank end will be the summation of all such small sections, the value of which is given by the definite integral, $\int_0^h 2l \, dh$. The relation between l and h is known in this case, and so the integral can be expressed in terms of one variable and evaluated. Because the limits are given in terms of h, it is best to substitute a function of h in place of l. From the given relation, $l = h^{\frac{1}{2}}/0.6$, and the integral can be written and evaluated as follows:

$$\int_0^h 2l \, dh = \frac{2}{0.6} \int_0^{h_1} h^{\frac{1}{2}} \, dh = \left(\frac{2}{3}\right)\left(\frac{2}{0.6}\right) [(h_1)^{\frac{3}{2}} - 0] = 2.22(h_1)^{\frac{3}{2}}$$
$$= (2.22)(3)^{\frac{3}{2}} = 11.6 \text{ ft}^2$$

Graphical Solutions

In many cases found in engineering practice the equation relating the variables concerned is not known, and it is complicated and difficult to determine. The appropriate integration can

still be carried out, but by graphical, rather than analytical, procedures.   In order to illustrate such an operation, consider the
record traced by a *recording flow meter*.   The pen of the meter
registers the instantaneous rate of flow of a fluid through the
meter.   The chart is moved at right angles to the flow-rate scale
by a clock mechanism.   The resulting record is a plot of flow
rate versus time on a rectangular coordinate system and would
appear as shown in Fig. 2-2.   A problem which arises in the use of
such a meter record is to find how much material has passed
through the system in some time period of interest to the operator, such as the hour of operation shown in the figure.

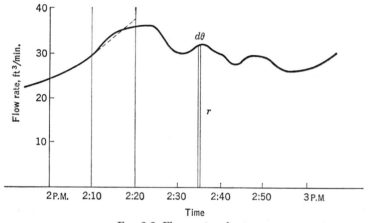

FIG. 2-2. Flow-meter chart.

For any very short time interval $d\theta$, the flow rate r can be considered substantially constant, and during that period the volume
of fluid passing through the meter is the product of the rate of
flow by the time period, or $r\,d\theta$.   Although the rates for suc-
ceeding periods are not the same, nevertheless a summation can
be made of all of the small sections of the figure to give the total
throughput for the hour of operation.   This quantity would be
$\int_{\theta_1}^{\theta_2} r\,d\theta$.   It is obvious, however, that r would prove to be a
complicated function of θ which would be difficult to evaluate
and perhaps to integrate.   Fortunately it is not difficult to carry
out the integration graphically on the chart itself.

The integral sought is equal to the area beneath the curve
between the times of 2 and 3 P.M.   Although it is not feasible
to divide this area into an infinite number of sections each having

an area of $r \, d\theta$, it is not difficult to divide the area into a limited number of sections, the area of each of which can be simply determined. Take as an example the area between the times 2:10 and 2:20. If the dashed line is drawn so that the two small areas between it and the curve are equal, the area below the straight line is the same as the area below the curve, and this area is equal to the mean ordinate of the dashed line multiplied by the time interval concerned.

A little practice makes it possible to judge the relative sizes of these small areas with reasonable accuracy, but if doubt remains, the time interval can be subdivided into two intervals. Because the curve during each of these is more nearly a straight line, less judgment is required to locate the dashed line for each. When the curve has marked curvature, it is better to take narrow sections, but in places where it is nearly straight, broader sections can be used to decrease the labor. It is usually more economical of time to take a few more sections than it is to bother trying to get the proper dashed lines for wider sections.

For the period between 2:10 and 2:20 the mean ordinate of the dashed line shown is 33.5, and so the volume of fluid passing through the meter in that interval is $(33.5 \text{ ft}^3/\text{min})(10 \text{ min}) = 335$ ft³. Summation of all the corresponding values for the sections chosen between 2 and 3 P.M. gives the total throughput sought.

Trial Solutions

The solution of engineering problems sometimes requires the handling of equations containing the third or higher power of an unknown quantity. These equations offer difficulty if a purely analytical solution is attempted. Nevertheless they can be solved without undue difficulty by trial methods. Unless a systematic approach is used, much time can be lost in random hunting. The technique of solution of such an equation will be illustrated by an example.

Example 2-A. The following equation is to be solved and a value or values for x obtained:

$$x^3 - 5.2x^2 - 25.9x - 14.2 = 0$$

Solution. By substituting whole number values which are easily raised to various powers, the situation can be explored rapidly. Using $x = +1$, the left-hand side of the equation becomes -44.3, and it may be seen that this negative difference from zero would be lessened by increasing the value assigned to x. Next try $x = 10$, which gives $+1000 - 520 - 259 - 14 = 0$, or $+207 = 0$. From this result it follows that one value of x lies between 1 and 10. One might try linear interpolation, either arithmetically or graphically, to obtain a closer value, but by inspection of the original equation it can be seen that the one positive term, x^3, increases more slowly near 1 than it does at higher values of x. Therefore, let us try a whole number nearer 10 than 1. Using 8, we obtain $512 - 333 - 217 - 14 = 0$, or $-52 = 0$. This value narrows the possible range considerably, and linear interpolation between 8 and 10 gives an indicated value of 8.4. When this value is substituted, there is obtained $+592.5 - 367.0 - 217.5 - 14.2 = 0$, or $-6.2 = 0$. This shows that the value chosen for x is slightly low. Trying next $x = 8.5$, the equation becomes $+614.0 - 375.5 - 220 - 14.2 = 0$, or $+4.3 = 0$. Linear interpolation over this still narrower range indicates that $x = 8.46$, and this value can be considered to be close enough as an approximation.

More than one root for this equation is to be expected. The equation shows that greater positive values than the one found will not satisfy it. The next step is to repeat the process just followed, using negative numbers. Trying $x = -10$ gives $-1000 - 520 + 259 - 14.2 = 0$, or $-1275 = 0$, showing that, with the first and second terms negative, x will have to be relatively small numerically. For $x = -1$, then $-1 - 5.2 + 25.9 - 14.2 = 0$, or $+5.5 = 0$; whereas $x = 0$ gives $-14.2 = 0$. It would thus appear that there might be one root between -10 and -1 and another between -1 and 0.

The value of x between -10 and -1 appears to be much nearer the latter value.

Using $x = -2$ gives $-8 - 20.8 + 5.8 - 14.2 = 0$, or $+8.8 = 0$
Using $x = -3$ gives $-27 - 46.8 + 77.7 - 14.2 = 0$, or $-10.3 = 0$
Using $x = -2.5$ gives $-15.6 - 32.5 + 64.4 - 14.2 = 0$, or $+2.1 = 0$
Using $x = -2.7$ gives $-19.7 - 37.9 + 69.9 - 14.2 = 0$, or $-1.9 = 0$

Therefore x may be taken equal to -2.62 as a reasonable approximation of the correct value.

Similarly for the third root, interpolation between 0 and -1 indicates -0.7 as a probable value.

Using $x = -0.7$ gives $-0.34 - 2.55 + 18.13 - 14.2 = 0$, or $+1.04 = 0$
Using $x = -0.6$ gives $-0.216 - 1.87 + 15.54 - 14.2 = 0$, or $-0.75 = 0$

Interpolation between these values gives $x = -0.64$ as a good approximation.

The three roots found indicate that the original equation can be factored to give $(x - 8.46)(x + 0.64)(x + 2.62) = 0$. When these factors are multiplied as a check on the work there is obtained $x^3 - 5.22x^2 - 25.89x - 14.18 = 0$. This is as close an approximation of the original equation as one might expect from approximate root values.

If certain conditions of the problem in hand precluded either positive or negative roots, the work involved in the solution of the problem would have been lessened. With the equation used here, interpolation over relatively wide ranges did not give dependable indications of the correct value, and the trial of simple whole number values chosen by inspection served better to narrow the uncertainty to a range in which linear interpolation was adequate. If three trial values are obtained, they can be plotted on coordinate paper and a smooth curve (not necessarily a straight line as in linear interpolation) drawn through them. The point where this line crosses the zero axis for the value obtained for the left-hand side of the equation will give a good indication of the next value to try. The question as to whether graphical three-point interpolation or additional trials without formal interpolation is more economical of time is one that each person needs to answer from his own experience.

Graphical Representation of Data

The advantages obtained from the use of graphical methods in recording and in using experimental physical and chemical data have resulted in the availability of ruled coordinate or graph paper of numerous varieties. The types differ in size of sheet, units used in the coordinate scales, fineness of subdivision by lines of the coordinate grid, semitransparency or opacity of the paper, and other characteristics.

The most common graphs are on rectangular or cartesian coordinates, and the most useful for general purposes have either 20 lines to the inch or 10 lines to the centimeter, the former being most common. The task of plotting some function of a variable would be aided if a paper were available with one coordinate axis laid out in terms of that function rather than the variable itself. When one considers all the possible functions in which there might be occasional interest, it can be seen that it would not pay to prepare special coordinate paper for more than a few of them. If such special paper is not available, it becomes necessary to calculate the desired function for each value of the pertinent variable, and to plot these calculated values on the standard uniform-scale paper. In a few cases, however, a particular function occurs so frequently in scientific and engineering calculations that it is economically feasible to prepare special coordinate papers.

One such commonly met function is the logarithm of the value of the variable, and several types of sheets are available based on this function. In "semilog" paper, one coordinate axis is the normal uniform scale, whereas the other, although labeled with the numbers, is spaced in accordance with the common logarithm (to the base 10) of the number. This scale is convenient in that it saves looking up the logarithms and tabulating them before plotting. This paper would be used in cases which called for plotting the logarithm of one variable against the other variable itself. Frequently it is useful to plot the logarithm of the first variable against the logarithm of the second variable, and for this purpose "log-log" papers are available. The logarithmic scales have the convenience mentioned above and they serve to "compress" a wide range of data into the much smaller range of logarithms. They have the disadvantages that they are not so sensitive in plotting small variations and that the divisions are not uniformly spaced, thus making accurate interpolation more difficult.

A problem often arises concerning the best way to plot a systematic series of results from experimental measurements. Let us say, for example, that measurements of variable A have been made at a series of values of variable B, other variables being kept constant throughout, and that the corresponding sets of values obtained are those listed in Table 2-1.

TABLE 2-1. EXPERIMENTAL DATA

Variable A	Variable B	Variable A	Variable B
1.60	1.10	4.95	4.25
2.04	1.63	5.80	4.60
2.40	2.25	6.50	5.10
2.95	2.75	7.25	5.25
3.50	3.30	8.00	5.65
4.30	3.70	9.05	5.90

A plot of these values on ordinary rectangular coordinate paper is shown in the upper part of Fig. 2-3. If each of these points were connected by lines to the points adjacent to it, a very irregular line would result for the whole set of values. If it is known that the behavior being studied would be expected to give a regular continuous relationship between the variables, it is justifiable to assume that the irregularities result from uncertainties in the experimental measurements. In this case, one draws a smooth curve which seems to fit best the trend indicated by the points. In the example in question, the resulting line turns out to be markedly curved, rising rather steeply at the

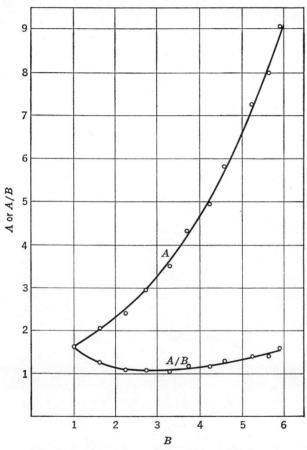

FIG. 2-3. Comparison of two ordinate functions.

upper end. Both these features are detrimental to accurate plotting and to subsequent interpolation.

Another method of plotting might be used in order to obviate these difficulties. For example, inspection shows that, if A/B were used in place of A as the ordinate, the range of values to be handled would be decreased, and so a correspondingly more sensitive scale could be used with the same size of paper. A plot of this function, without changing the ordinate scale, is shown in the lower part of Fig. 2-3. The curve drawn in this case corresponds directly to the curve chosen in the original plot. It can be seen that the new variable does have a much smaller range of values, and, on the same paper, the distance between 1 and 2 on the ordinate axis could be made ten times as large. One of the disadvantages of the original plot has thus been obviated, but the line drawn is still markedly curved.

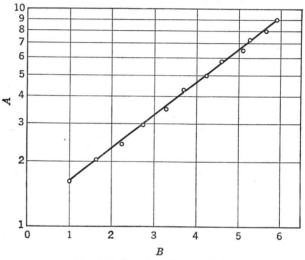

Fig. 2-4. Semilogarithmic plot.

Still another method of plotting is resorted to in Fig. 2-4. Instead of using the function A/B, the logarithm to the base ten of A is the ordinate, and semilog paper is used as a convenience. In this plot, the points and the line correspond directly to those of the original plot. The curve has now become essentially a straight line. This fact represents a great advantage in interpolation, and it also serves to indicate a simple analytical relationship existing among the data. The behavior in this case can be described by an equation of the form of $\log A = cB + d$, in which the constants c and d can be determined as to numerical value and sign from the plot. When these evaluations are made for the curve in Fig. 2-4, the equation becomes $\log A = 0.1509B + 0.0585$. It should be noted that, although the equation for the line may be precise, it does not represent the facts any better than the line drawn through the experimental points describes the behavior of the system under study.

Different assemblages of experimental results would call for different types of plots for best results, but the general procedures presented here suggest ways of attacking a problem. Of the various types of special coordinate paper available, mention may be made of a triangular grid which is useful in plotting compositions of mixtures of three components, a rectangular grid with the inverse value of one variable, and a circular grid for polar coordinates.

Example 2-B. It is often convenient to know a mean value of some function of a variable with respect to another variable in a given range of association. The mean value can be defined as that value which, if used as a constant, when multiplied by the increment of the other variable within the range of association gives a product equal to an integrated value. For example, consider the mean value of u^2 over a range of r from zero to unity on the basis of the following data.

r	u	r	u
0	5.00	0.6	3.20
0.1	4.95	0.7	2.55
0.2	4.81	0.8	1.82
0.3	4.54	0.9	0.95
0.4	4.20	1.0	0
0.5	3.74		

The mean value can be obtained from the equation

$$(u^2)_{\text{mean}} = \frac{\int_{r_1}^{r_2} u^2 \, dr}{\int_{r_1}^{r_2} dr} = \frac{\int_{r_1}^{r_2} u^2 \, dr}{\Delta r}$$

From this relation it can be seen that

$$(u^2)_{\text{mean}} \, \Delta r = \int_{r_1}^{r_2} u^2 \, dr$$

and thus the value of $(u^2)_{\text{mean}}$ serves the purpose described above.

Solution. For the case in question, evaluation of $(u^2)_{\text{mean}}$ calls for determination of the value of the integral shown above in terms of the relationship between u and r represented by the given data. If the data are plotted directly, Fig. 2-B1 is obtained. It can be seen that u varies markedly with changing r and that a mean value of u^2 is not directly evident. Because the mean value of u^2, rather than u, is desired, it is necessary to plot corresponding values of u^2 versus r as in Fig. 2-B2 and to determine the area between the curve and the r axis of coordinates. This area corresponds to $\int u^2 \, dr$, and $(u^2)_{\text{mean}}$ can be taken equal to $(\int u^2 \, dr)/\Delta r$.

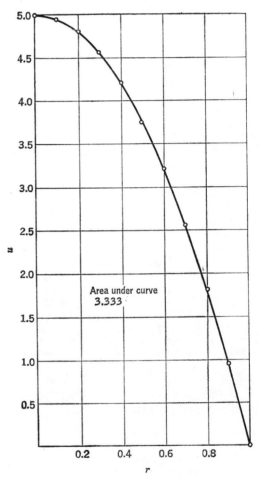

FIG. 2-B1. Plot of u versus r.

Another method of determining $(u^2)_{\text{mean}}$ depends upon recognizing that the curve in Fig. 2-B1 appears to be a parabola, which would have an equation of the form $u = a(b - r^2)$, in which a and b are constants. The applicability of the parabolic equation to the given data can be easily tested. When $r = 1$, $r^2 = 1$, $u = 0$, and so $b = 1$. When $r = 0$, $r^2 = 0$, $u = 5.00 = a$. The equation takes the form $u = (5)(1 - r^2)$

and can be tested with other pairs of values. When $r = 0.3$, $u = (5)(1 - 0.09) = (5)(0.91) = 4.55$. When $r = 0.6$, $u = (5)(1 - 0.36) = (5)(0.64) = 3.20$. Not only do these values agree with the tabulated ones as well as could be expected of experimental data but all the other

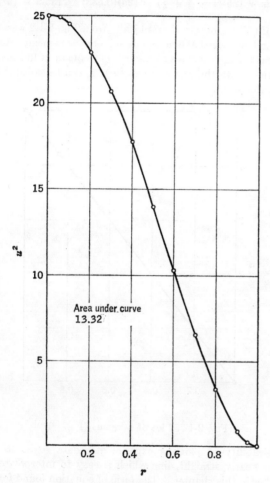

Area under curve
13.32

FIG. 2-B2. Plot of u^2 versus r.

pairs agree also, and the equation is thus found to express with adequate accuracy the relation between u and r.

This equation can now be used to evaluate the desired quantity,
$$\int_{r=0}^{r=1} u^2 \, dr/\Delta r = \int_0^1 u^2 \, dr/(1 - 0) = \int_0^1 u^2 \, dr, \text{ by the following steps:}$$

$$u^2 = (25)(1 - r^2)^2$$
$$u^2 \, dr = (25)(1 - 2r^2 + r^4) \, dr$$
$$\int_{r_1}^{r_2} u^2 \, dr = (25)[(r_2 - r_1) - \tfrac{2}{3}(r_2^3 - r_1^3) + \tfrac{1}{5}(r_2^5 - r_1^5)]$$
$$\int_0^1 u^2 \, dr = (25)(1 - \tfrac{2}{3} + \tfrac{1}{5}) = (25)(0.533) = 13.33 = (u^2)_{\text{mean}}$$

The value of $(u^2)_{\text{mean}}$ obtained graphically from Fig. 2-B2 was 13.32.

The method employed above to obtain a pertinent mean value, which can be used as though constant in value, is of frequent utility in engineering calculations. In the case treated, $(u^2)_{\text{mean}}$ can be called the "mean effective" value of u^2.

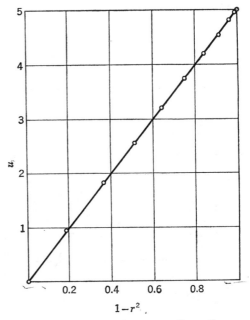

FIG. 2-B3. Plot of u versus $(1 - r^2)$.

The desirability of plotting experimental data so as to obtain a straight, or nearly straight, line which is easy to interpolate was discussed earlier in this chapter. The form of equation found for the data in the tabulation suggests a plot of u versus $(1 - r^2)$. This plot is shown in Fig. 2-B3, and it gives a straight line having a slope of 5 as predicted by the equation. In this case, the plot gives no information beyond that furnished by the equation already known, but it serves to illustrate an additional case in which suitable sets of coordinates can be found which will tend to give nearly straight-line plots. Such a plot is primarily useful for purposes of interpolation or judicious extrapolation.

One special use of a straight-line plot beyond increasing ease of extrapolation or interpolation is in ready establishment of slopes by graphical
means.   For example, the determination of slopes in Fig. 2-B1 near the
value of $r = 0$ is not easily done with precision when using graphical
techniques because as r approaches zero, small errors in placing the
straightedge tangent to the curve give large percentage errors in the
values of the slopes.   A straight-line plot such as that shown in Fig.
2-B3, however, allows a ready reading of the slope of u versus $(1 - r^2)$.
This slope is the quantity a in the equation $u = a(1 - r^2)$.   When a
is known, the equation can be used to evaluate du/dr by differentiation,
because $du/dr = -2ar$.   That value of du/dr is more precise than a
slope read from Fig. 2-B1.

3

Engineering Measurements

There are a few types of quantitative measurements which play an important part in engineering activities. They are closely associated with the fundamental concepts discussed earlier: that is, force, length, time, and temperature. The characteristics of an engineering system which are most frequently involved in appraisals of performance are lengths, quantities of material involved, pressures, temperatures, times, and quantities of energy.

Length

The ability to measure lengths or distances is a basic necessity for almost all the physical determinations used in engineering practice. Many interesting and ingenious methods have been devised for precise comparison of lengths of objects with each other, and ultimately with the accepted standard of length used in defining the unit in use. Such methods are well enough known to students of science that they need not be dwelt upon here. The measurement of length makes possible the determination of areas and volumes.

Quantity of Material

Determinations of quantities of material are usually made in terms of *weight*, which represents a *force*. Weight can be determined by comparison of the force exerted by gravity on the body in question with the force exerted on standard bodies or "weights." The standardization or calibration of these weights is referred back ultimately to the force exerted by standard gravity upon the accepted standard mass which is the reference basis in the mass system of units. This comparison of forces can be made in terms of their effects in distorting a spring or similar mechanism or through balancing techniques utilizing beams. As long as gravitational acceleration remains constant, the weight of a body is directly proportional to its mass and thus serves as a convenient measure of it under those conditions. For most engineering purposes, then, the weight in pounds of a body can be used as a relative measure of its mass, although it must be remembered that this weight dimensionally is different from mass.

Pressure

The pressure exerted on a surface is defined as the *force* acting upon a unit area and would be expressed as pounds per square foot. Because this unit involves a relatively large area and gives large numerical values for commonplace pressures, the more customary unit of measurement is pounds per square inch. These two units are frequently abbreviated for convenience to psf and psi, respectively. Pressure is used primarily to characterize the behavior of fluids (liquids and gases). In a continuous, stationary body of fluid, the pressure exerted by any small section of it upon an adjacent portion is the same at all points in the fluid that are at the same elevation, and the pressure at any one point in the fluid is the same in all directions. These facts are in accordance with *Newton's second law of motion* which states that in the case of a body at rest the forces applied to it are in balance, or the net force is zero. If the forces differed from point to point in a horizontal plane, there would be flow from regions of higher to those of lower pressure, and the fluid would not be static. The principle calling for a state of rest when forces upon the system are in balance applies also to a solid body and is a basic concept in engineering practice. For example, reliance upon this principle underlies the methods of measuring weight discussed above.

On the other hand, the pressure in a static fluid is not the same for different points in a vertical plane, but varies because of the varying weight of fluid above the point in question and the corresponding force thus exerted from above. In a gas, this variation of pressure with elevation is relatively small compared to total pressures ordinarily met, and it is often neglected in calculations. Because of the much greater specific weights of liquids, however, this effect can seldom be overlooked when liquids are involved. If it were not for gravity, the pressure would be the same in all parts of a static body of fluid.

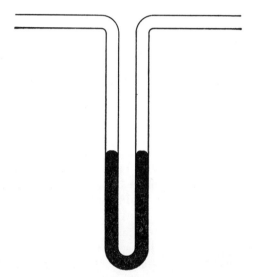

FIG. 3-1. Manometer.

One of the simplest ways of measuring the pressure exerted by a fluid on the walls of its container is by use of a *manometer*. It consists of a tube in the form of a U, which is partially filled with a liquid, as shown in Fig. 3-1. If the temperature is uniform throughout the liquid, and the pressure, or the force per unit area, at the surface of the liquid in each limb of the tube is the same, the two menisci will come to rest at the same level or elevation, no matter what the relative sizes of the two limbs may be, if each tube is large enough to avoid marked capillary effect. If one of the balanced forces in the manometer is changed, the state of rest is disturbed, and motion in the system will be induced until forces are again balanced and a new state of rest is attained. Thus, if the pressure in one arm of the manometer is increased above that in the other, the liquid surfaces will move until the forces per unit area are again balanced. By the principle outlined above, it can be seen that the pressure at the lower meniscus must be the same as that in the other arm at a point in the same horizontal plane, or further movement of the meniscus would occur. The pressure at this point, however, is greater than the pressure at the upper meniscus by the force per unit area caused by the column of liquid above the point. The difference in elevations of the two menisci serves then as a measure of the difference in pressure between the spaces above the menisci.

In most cases one arm will be connected by tubing to the vessel in which it is desired to measure the pressure, the other arm being left open to the atmosphere. The difference in level of the menisci thus represents the difference in pressure between the vessel and the atmosphere. In order to ascertain the actual pressure in the vessel from this difference it is necessary to know the atmospheric pressure. This pressure is determined by means of a *barometer*, which is merely a mercury manometer so arranged that one arm is open to the atmosphere, and the other arm is pumped out to a high vacuum, corresponding closely to zero pressure. If the air is exactly at 1 atm of pressure, the barometer will show a difference in levels of 29.9 in. (760 mm), and this corresponds to a pressure difference of 14.7 psi. Let us suppose that the manometer attached to the vessel mentioned above contains water as the liquid, that one arm is open to the atmosphere, and that the difference in levels is 10 in., the difference indicating that the pressure in the vessel is greater than atmospheric. This manometer reading can be converted to an equivalent height of mercury column (10/13.6 = 0.735 in.), in which 13.6 is the specific gravity of mercury relative to water at the same temperature, or to psi [(0.735/29.9)(14.7) = 0.36 psi].

Because most pressure gauges indicate only a difference from existing atmospheric pressure, the reading is known as "gauge pressure," and the pressure in the vessel discussed above would be designated as 0.36 pound per square inch gauge, or 0.36 psig. In order to determine the actual pressure in the vessel, the value of atmospheric pressure must be added to the gauge pressure (in consistent units, of course). Thus the actual or "absolute" pressure in the case considered would be either

$$0.735 + 29.9 = 30.64 \text{ in. Hg abs}$$

or 0.36 + 14.7 = 15.06 pounds per square inch absolute (psia). It can be seen that there is a marked difference between the gauge pressure and the absolute pressure. In some calculations one may be pertinent, and in different calculations the other, but in any event care must be taken that the proper value is used. The differences among absolute pressure, gauge pressure, and "vacuum" are shown graphically in Fig. 3-2. Vacuum is measured downward from atmospheric pressure, usually in in. Hg.

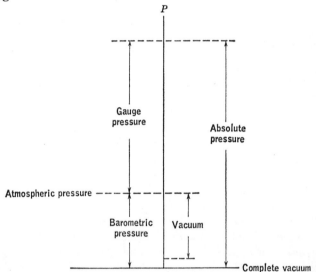

Fig. 3-2. Basis for pressure measurements.

In the manometer with one arm open to the atmosphere, the fluid filling the other arm connected to the vessel in which the pressure is to be measured may be air or another gas, or it may be a liquid which is immiscible with the liquid used in the manometer.   Take as an example the measurement of pressure in a tank containing oil using a mercury manometer, as indicated in Fig. 3-3.   If the connecting line is filled with a gas, the difference in pressure between the tank and the gas-mercury interface in the manometer as a result of the height of the connecting column of gas is likely to be small enough to neglect, in comparison to the magnitude of pressure in the tank.   On the other hand, if the connecting line is filled with oil, the pressure difference resulting from the oil column involved is likely to be too large to

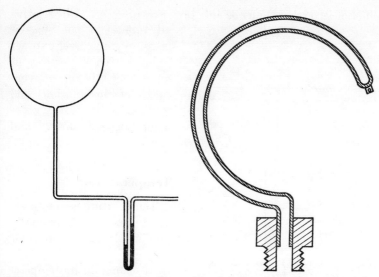

FIG. 3-3. Effect of connecting line   FIG. 3-4. Bourdon pressure element.
upon manometer reading.

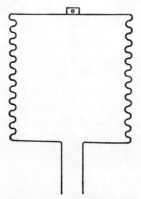

FIG. 3-5. Bellows or aneroid pressure element.

ignore, and, in order to ascertain the pressure in the tank from
the manometer reading, a correction must be made for the effect
of the oil in the connecting line.

There are many other types of pressure-measuring devices such
as the three types of pressure-sensitive elements shown in Figs.
3-4, 3-5, 3-6, which are, respectively, the Bourdon (or bent flexible
tube) gauge, the bellows gauge, and the dead-weight gauge.
Nearly all such devices, like the manometer, indicate pressure

differences, rather than absolute pressures directly.   The relative advantages of one type of pressure gauge over another lie in such characteristics as range, sensitivity, convenience of installation and reading, ruggedness, accuracy, dependability, and cost.

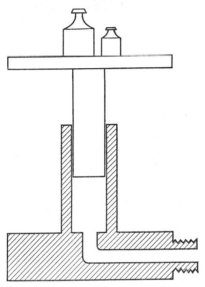

FIG. 3-6. Dead-weight pressure element.

Temperature

Temperature is most commonly measured by determining the effect on some property of matter caused by a change in its temperature.   Changes in volume or length are the most common indicators, examples being the familiar mercury-in-glass thermometer and the bimetallic strip thermometer, utilizing differences in the thermal expansion of two materials to cause a deflection of the movable end of the strip shown in Fig. 3-7. Instruments in which the change in fluid pressure within a constant-volume vessel serves to indicate temperature change are often used.   One device of this type relies on the change in vapor pressure of a volatile liquid.   Another system of temperature measurement depends on electrical behavior such as the

FIG. 3-7. Bimetallic temperature element.

change in electromotive force generated at a junction of two dissimilar electric conductors (thermocouple) or the change in electrical resistance of a conductor or semiconductor (resistance thermometer, thermistor).   At high temperatures the change in intensity of radiation emitted by a hot body (optical pyrometer) may be used to establish the temperature.

All these instruments require calibration in terms of known

temperature standards, and a series of "fixed points" on the temperature scale has been carefully standardized. These reproducible points correspond mostly to melting or boiling points of purified substances and are chosen to provide a relatively good distribution of temperatures over the whole working scale.

A number of different arbitrary scales have been devised to indicate quantitatively the temperature of a body. The two scales commonly used are based upon the choice of two easily reproducible states as fixed points on the scale, and then upon division of the temperature interval between them into a chosen number of equal divisions called *degrees*. Although both common scales use the same fixed points, they unfortunately differ in the number of divisions, or the magnitude of the degree, chosen. The fixed points are the temperature of equilibrium between ice and water in contact with air at 1 atm and the boiling temperature of water at 1 atm pressure. The *centigrade scale* divides this temperature interval into 100 divisions (°C), whereas the *Fahrenheit scale* uses 180 divisions (°F). To add to the confusion thus caused, the ice-water point is given the temperature value of 0° on the centigrade scale, but 32° on the Fahrenheit scale. This brings the normal boiling point for water at 100°C and 212°F, respectively.

The fact that the pressure-volume product for any perfect gas is a function only of temperature serves as the basis for another type of temperature scale. The equation describing the behavior of one mole of a perfect gas is written $PV = \mathbf{R}T$. Because $\mathbf{R}$ is a constant, the PV product is seen to be directly proportional to the quantity T. In order that the equation shall describe the behavior of a given perfect gas, the values of T must be chosen so that T is directly proportional to PV at any state, and also so that T approaches zero as the PV product approaches zero. This sort of a temperature scale is called the *perfect-gas scale*. The magnitude of the unit division or degree on such a scale is not fixed by the equation and can be arbitrarily chosen. The zero point on any scale is fixed, however, at that state where $PV = 0$. For convenience, two different perfect-gas scales are in common use, having degree sizes the same as the centigrade and Fahrenheit scales, respectively. The former is called the *Kelvin scale* (°K) and the latter the *Rankine scale* (°R). The names were given to honor men who contributed greatly to studies of temperature through thermodynamics.

It is interesting to note that the state to which the PV product for a perfect gas can be extrapolated to give a zero value leads to the same perfect-gas zero of temperature, regardless of the identity of the perfect gas. This point on the perfect-gas, or absolute temperature, scale has wider significance in that it appears to be the lower limit of temperatures physically attainable in the laboratory, and also the temperature at which the gas molecules are at their lowest energy level.   It appears, therefore,

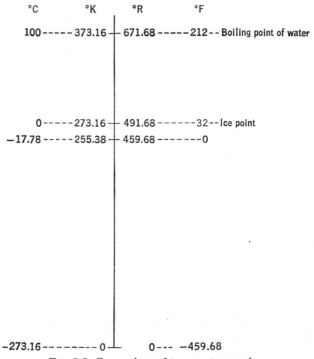

FIG. 3-8. Comparison of temperature scales.

to be the fixed point upon which to base temperature scales having absolute significance rather than purely arbitrary values.

The relative values of the temperatures of the fixed points discussed above are shown in Fig. 3-8 on each of the scales which have been outlined.   It is not surprising to find that the arbitrarily chosen temperatures on the centigrade and Fahrenheit scales turn out to be odd values on the corresponding absolute scales.   These odd values are rounded off to whole numbers for most engineering calculations.   It should be kept in mind in calculations that the zero values on the centigrade and Fahrenheit scales are not the same temperature.

Time

Time standards are based primarily on astronomical events, and standard time signals are available over radio circuits. These signals can be utilized for calibration of chronometers, clocks, and other mechanical devices for indicating time. Recently, with growth of interest in exceedingly short time periods, standards have been developed to utilize the characteristic frequency of vibration in quartz crystals and also that of the atoms in the ammonia molecule. With the application of synchronous electric motors to the drive of clocks, together with the careful monitoring of generator frequencies in power plants on this account, very convenient time measurements can be made for engineering work. Sudden heavy changes of load on the generators, however, can cause temporary variations in frequency and result in local errors in time measurement. Independent time standards, such as quartz oscillators, give more dependable measurements.

Energy

The determination of the amount of energy contained in, or characteristic of, an engineering system is exceedingly difficult, and measurements are primarily limited to amounts of energy entering or leaving such systems. For example, the energy added to water in a boiler to produce steam can be measured, as can the amount of energy developed mechanically from the steam in a turbine, but the total amount of energy contained in one pound of water at a given state is not known on an absolute basis, and for engineering purposes need not be known.

The energy leaving a system may be absorbed or utilized in the accomplishment of some task for which the energy requirement is known. If energy is leaving a system because the surroundings are at a lower temperature, it may be transferred to a known amount of water and the temperature rise of this water noted. The Btu as a unit of energy is defined in terms of such a process, and so the amount of energy transferred from the system can be determined from this type of measurement. Energy addition to a system may be demonstrated by the passage of current through an electrical resistance element submerged in a liquid. The energy will cause a rise of temperature in the heater, and this will cause energy transfer to the cooler liquid which in turn will rise in temperature. The amount of energy added can be determined from electrical measurements of the voltage drop across the resistance element and the number of coulombs passed.

Example 3-A. A large open-topped tank contains an acid solution at room temperature. Connected to the bottom of the tank is a vertical pipe extending downward to a point A which is 50 ft lower than the surface of the acid in the tank. There the pipe turns and extends horizontally for 100 ft, then runs vertically upward a distance of 25 ft to a point B where there is a closed valve. A Bourdon pressure gauge is attached to the pipe at point A, and it shows a reading of 28.0 psi. What is the specific weight of the acid in lb/ft³, and its specific gravity at the prevailing temperature compared to water with a specific weight of 62.3 lb/ft³? What is the absolute pressure in the pipe at point B?

Solution. The valve at point B is closed, and so there will be no flow through the pipe, and the fluid in the system is static. The reading of the Bourdon gauge represents the difference between the pressure in the pipe at point A and that in the atmosphere outside the pipe. Considering the relatively small differences in elevation involved in this example, both atmospheric pressure and the acceleration resulting from gravity can be considered to be constant. Because the tank is open and atmospheric pressure is applied to the liquid surface, the pressure reading of the gauge corresponds directly to the pressure exerted by a column of liquid 50 ft high.

If σ is the specific weight of the acid in lb/ft³, a cube of the acid 1 ft on a side would weigh σ lb and would exert a pressure on its bottom face of σ psf. Thus a static column of this acid 1 ft high exerts a pressure of σ psf or $(\sigma/144)$ psi. A column 50 ft high exerts a pressure of $(50\sigma/144)$ psi. Equating the two values for the absolute pressure at point A, balancing out the effect of atmospheric pressure there and at the surface in the tank,

$$\frac{50\sigma}{144} + p_{\text{atm}} = 28.0 + p_{\text{atm}}$$

From this equation,

$$\sigma = \frac{(28.0)(144)}{50} = 80.7 \text{ lb/ft}^3$$

Checking this expression dimensionally,

$$\sigma = \frac{(\text{lb/in.}^2)(\text{in.}^2/\text{ft}^2)}{\text{ft}} = \frac{\text{lb/ft}^2}{\text{ft}} = \frac{\text{lb}}{\text{ft}^3}$$

The specific gravity of the acid referred to water is the ratio of their specific weights.

$$\text{sp gr}_{\text{acid}} = \frac{80.7}{62.3} = 1.296 \qquad \text{dimensionless}$$

The horizontal run of pipe contributes no change in static pressure, and so the pressure at point B corresponds to a column of liquid $50 - 25 = 25$ ft high. The pressure resulting from this column $(25/144)(80.7) = 14.0$ psi. In order to obtain the absolute pressure at point B, the pressure from the atmosphere must be added. Assuming that a normal barometric pressure exists at the time, the absolute pressure at B is $14.0 + 14.7 = 28.7$ psia.

Example 3-B. A pipeline is carrying a liquid with a specific gravity of 1.25 compared to water at room temperature. Connected to the side of this pipe is a line of metal tubing which runs 100 ft horizontally, and then vertically upward to connect to a mercury manometer in a control room. The tubing from the pipeline to the surface of mercury of one limb of the manometer is completely filled with the liquid flowing in the pipeline. The other limb of the manometer is open to the atmosphere. The two limbs have the same diameter. When both mercury surfaces are at the same level, they are exactly 12 ft higher than the tubing connection to the pipe. When the mercury meniscus in the open limb is 24 in. higher than that in the other limb, what is the pressure in the tubing at its connection to the pipeline?

Solution. When the fluids in the manometer have come to rest, there will be no flow in the tubing, and static conditions apply. Because the two limbs of the manometer have equal diameters, any shift from a position of equal levels will result in one meniscus moving downward the same distance as the other meniscus moves upward. Thus the downward movement of the first meniscus will be one-half of the final difference of level of the two menisci.

The absolute pressure in the tubing at the pipeline connections will be balanced by and thus equal to the atmospheric pressure on the open manometer limb plus the pressure resulting from a column of mercury 24 in. high plus that from a column of pipeline liquid which is $12 - (24)/(2)(12) = 12 - 1 = 11$ ft high. Take the specific gravity of mercury as 13.6 compared to water with a specific weight of 62.3 lb/ft³.

$$P = P_{\text{atm}} + \left(\frac{24}{12}\right)(13.6)\left(\frac{62.3}{144}\right) + (11)(1.25)\left(\frac{62.3}{144}\right)$$

Assume $P_{\text{atm}} = 14.7$ psi.

$$P = 14.7 + 11.77 + 5.95 = 14.7 + 17.7 = 32.4 \text{ psia or } 17.7 \text{ psig}$$

Example 3-C. A thermally insulated pressure vessel of constant volume was completely filled with a liquid at 70°F, requiring 10.21 lb of liquid. Direct current was passed through an electric heating element immersed in the liquid for a period of 100 sec at 24 volts and 8.2 amp. The temperature of the liquid, after it had become uniform, had risen by 2.02°F. What is the heat capacity of the liquid in Btu/(lb)(°F)?

For this liquid, the coefficient of thermal expansion, $\left(\dfrac{dV}{dt}\right)\left(\dfrac{1}{V}\right)$, is 4.00×10^{-4} °F^{-1} and the coefficient of compressibility, $\left(\dfrac{dV}{dP}\right)\left(\dfrac{1}{V}\right)$, is 3.40×10^{-6} psi^{-1}. What change in pressure occurred in the vessel as a result of the change in temperature?

Solution. In accordance with the units given, the heat capacity is the energy required to raise the temperature of 1 lb of the material by 1°F. Because the vessel does not change in volume, the heat capacity determined in this case would be called the heat capacity at constant volume C_V.

The energy added to the system was

$$\frac{(24)(8.2)(100)}{(1000)(3600)} = 0.00546 \text{ kwhr}$$

Using the conversion factor given in Table 1-2 (p. 6), this amount of energy corresponds to $(0.00546)(3412) = 18.66$ Btu. Then

$$C_V = \frac{18.66}{(10.21)(2.02)} = 0.905 \frac{\text{Btu}}{\text{(lb)(°F)}}$$

$$\frac{\text{Coefficient of thermal expansion}}{\text{Coefficient of compressibility}} =$$

$$\frac{(dV/dt)(1/V)}{(dV/dP)(1/V)} = \frac{dP}{dt} \qquad \text{when volume is constant}$$

Therefore, $dP/dt = (4.00 \times 10^{-4})/(3.40 \times 10^{-6}) = 117.7$ psi/°F. For the small change in temperature involved $\Delta P/\Delta T$ may be taken equal to dP/dt. Then the increase in pressure in the vessel $= (117.7)(2.02) = 238$ psi.

4

Behavior of Gases

Gases are of major importance in industrial chemical processes as reactants, intermediates, or products. The volume occupied by a given weight of gas varies widely with the temperature and pressure, as well as with the composition of the gas. Although, when considered on the basis of high precision, every gas differs from the others in its quantitative behavior, there are some simple relationships which hold approximately for gases in general. The degree of deviation from these simple laws of gas behavior varies from one substance to another, and from one set of conditions of temperature and pressure to another for any one gas. Nevertheless, many occasions are encountered in industry when the laws, as expressed by the perfect-gas equation, will predict behavior within sufficiently close limits of error to make them very useful when detailed and accurate data are not available from experimental measurements. The conditions which are more favorable for close adherence to the simple gas laws are lower pressure, higher temperature, and greater remoteness from condensation.

Perfect Gases

For any gas which follows perfect-gas laws it can be said that *one pound-molecular weight* (lb mole or mole) when kept at 32°F (460 + 32 = 492°R) and a pressure of 1 atm (14.7 psia or 29.9 in. Hg abs) occupies a volume of 359 ft³, which is the standard molal volume. The volume varies in direct proportion to the absolute or Rankine-scale temperature, and inversely with the absolute pressure. Mole for mole, all such gases behave alike volumetrically, whether separate or in the form of mixtures. Gases meeting these requirements are designated as *perfect gases*. Their behavior is expressed by the familiar relation

$$PV = \mathbf{n}\mathbf{R}T \qquad (4\text{-}1)$$

in which V is the volume occupied by the sample of gas at pressure P and absolute temperature T, $\mathbf{n}$ is the number of moles in the sample, and $\mathbf{R}$ is the gas constant. The constant $\mathbf{R}$ depends in numerical value upon the units used for the other quantities. When the pressure is in psia, the volume in ft^3/lb mole, and the temperature in degrees Rankine, $\mathbf{R}$ has the *value* of 10.73 (psi) $(ft^3/lb)/(lb\ mole)(°R)$. Other values for $\mathbf{R}$ which are often used are 1.987 Btu/(lb mole)(°R), 1.987 g cal/(g mole)(°K), and 0.0821 (atm)(liter)/(g mole)(°K).

Equation (4-1) is general in its application to perfect gases, and the same value of $\mathbf{R}$ serves for all such gases. It is often convenient, however, to use the same relationship expressed in terms applying to a particular substance only. If the right-hand side of Eq. (4-1) is multiplied and divided by the molecular weight of the substance concerned, the equation becomes

$$PV = \mathbf{n}M \frac{\mathbf{R}}{M} T \qquad (4\text{-}2)$$

In common engineering units, $\mathbf{n}M$ is the number of pounds of the perfect gas, and $\mathbf{R}/M$, which is given the symbol b, is the *specific gas constant* for 1 lb of the particular gas. The equation can be written

$$PV = mbT \qquad (4\text{-}3)$$

For example, a sample consisting of 10 lb of nitrogen gas is to be stored in a container at 16 psia and 70°F, and it is desired to know how large a container would be required. Using Eq. (4-3), assuming that nitrogen under these conditions behaves as a perfect gas, and taking its molecular weight as 28,

$$(16)(V) = (10)(10.73/28)(460 + 70)$$

which gives $V = 127\ ft^3$. The same result is obtained, of course, by using Eq. (4-1) in terms of moles, the sample consisting of $10/28 = 0.357$ mole. The equation which results is

$$(16)(V) = (0.357)(10.73)(460 + 70)$$

and $V = 127$ ft^3 as before.

The value of 359 ft^3 for the standard molal volume, as given above, corresponds to the value of 22.4 liters, a quantity which is commonly encountered when dealing with metric units. For the calculation of the standard molal volume in engineering units, Eq. (4-1) may be used to give

$$(14.7)(V) = (1)(10.73)(460 + 32)$$

from which $V = 359.13$ ft^3, which is rounded off for convenience to the easily remembered value of 359 ft^3.

The volume occupied by a sample of perfect gas can be calculated using either Eq. (4-1) or Eq. (4-3), or it can be obtained by comparison of its volume under the given conditions with that at standard conditions. For example, a mole of nitrogen gas (N_2) at 90°F and 17.0 psia would occupy a volume of $(359) \left(\dfrac{460 + 90}{460 + 32} \right) \left(\dfrac{14.7}{17.0} \right) = 347$ ft^3. A mixture consisting of $\frac{1}{2}$ mole of N_2 and $\frac{1}{2}$ mole of H_2 and giving 1 mole of gas mixture would occupy the same volume under the same conditions of temperature and pressure. The weight of nitrogen in the first sample would be a number of pounds equal to the molecular weight, or 28 lb. For the mixed sample the weight would be $(\frac{1}{2})(28) + (\frac{1}{2})(2.016) = 15.0$ lb. This mixture would then have a specific weight at the stated conditions of $15.0/347 = 0.043$ lb/ft^3 as compared to approximately 62.3 lb/ft^3 for liquid water.

This low value of specific weight for gases makes it difficult to measure that quantity directly, samples of reasonable size weighing so little. It is customary, therefore to measure quantities of gaseous substances by volume. This property has the added advantage that, for perfect gases under given conditions of temperature and pressure, volumes are proportional to numbers of moles present, and these quantities are directly useful when chemical reactions are involved.

Gas Mixtures

Under ideal conditions, when gases are mixed, the molecules of each kind will exert the same pressure as though they alone filled the whole space. From this it follows that the total pressure exerted by the mixture will equal the sum of these partial pressures of the different components present.   This relationship is known as *Dalton's law*, and it was based upon experimental observations covering only a limited range of conditions.   More extensive measurements have shown that major deviations appear under many conditions commonly encountered.   Dalton's law gives, nevertheless, a convenient approximation of the behavior of many gas mixtures under conditions found in industrial practice, and it will be used in discussions in this book.

In a mixture of perfect gases, the volume that each component would have at the existing temperature and total pressure can be calculated.   The sum of these volumes for all components present will equal the total volume of the mixture under those conditions, if Dalton's law applies.   If the volumes thus calculated for each of the components are divided by the total volume of the mixture, the values obtained represent the volume fractions of the components in the mixture.   These fractions multiplied by 100% give the volume percentages of the components in the mixture. Because all these values are calculated for the same conditions of temperature and pressure, the volumes found will be proportional to the number of moles present in each case.   For this reason, the volume fraction or percentage will also be equal to the mole fraction or percentage.   If these values and the molecular weights of the different components are known, the weight fractions can be calculated.   The weight fractions, however, are not ordinarily as useful as are the mole or volume fractions of gases.

Analysis of Gases

One of the most common ways of analyzing a gas mixture is to measure the volume occupied by the mixture at a given convenient temperature and pressure, and then, after removing one component by chemical or other means, remeasure the residual gas at the same temperature and pressure.   The decrease in volume divided by the original volume gives the volume or mole fraction of the removed component in the original mixture.   This process can be continued for as many of the other components as are capable of being removed one at a time.

Because the composition of gas mixtures is ordinarily determined on a volume basis and because volume fractions or mole fractions are the most useful values, gas analyses are almost

universally reported on this basis.   If a gas analysis is reported
without specific indication as to what unit of measurement is used,
it may be safely inferred that volume fraction or percentages are
meant.

Combustion Gases

Consider a gas mixture for which the following analysis is
reported: 14.2% CO_2, 6.7% O_2, and 79.1% N_2.   This gas, from
the analysis, might well be the product of a combustion process
obtained from a carbonaceous fuel burning in air.   For most
engineering purposes the composition of air can be taken as
20.9% O_2 and 79.1% N_2.   This represents a simplified represen-
tation, in which the inert gases, other than nitrogen, that occur
in relatively small percentages are classed for the sake of convenience as N_2.   This simplification does not cause an undue
error in most calculations.

In an ordinary combustion process very little of the nitrogen of
the air is affected, and so it remains practically unchanged in the
resulting gases.   On the other hand, O_2 will react and change its
molecular identity.   If it reacts with carbon, it may appear in the
form of CO or CO_2, the latter if combustion is complete, and a
mixture of the two oxides if combustion is only partially complete.
In the mixture reported above, it can be seen that the percentages
of the given components add up to 100, thus indicating that no
other component than those listed is present (an exception to this
conclusion in regard to water vapor will be discussed later).   The
analysis thus indicates that, in the case in question, combustion
was complete, and excess O_2 was provided by using an excess of
air over that theoretically required to burn the carbon, which is
represented in the mixture by CO_2.   When such a combustion
process occurs the chemical reaction can be written,

$$C(s) + O_2(g) \rightarrow CO_2(g)$$

in which the designation (s) indicates a *solid* and (g) a *gas*.   In
the work to follow, the mole will be taken as a weight in pounds
equal to the formula weight of the element or compound as used
in the equations involved.

From the above equation it can be seen that for each mole of
CO_2 produced 1 mole of O_2 would disappear as such.   The flue-
gas analysis cited above shows that for each 79.1 moles of N_2

present there are 20.9 moles of O_2 accounted for, either as O_2 or as CO_2. This proportion corresponds to that in air, and so it can be concluded that the reaction shown in the equation above is the only change that has occurred, and the process involved is the combustion of carbon.

Calculations Based upon Gas Analyses

In making process calculations it becomes necessary to choose a basis upon which to work. For the process under discussion this basis might be, for example, either 1 mole of C, 1 lb of C, 100 moles of air, 0.791 mole of N_2, or any other arbitrarily chosen amount of material. The choice should be made so that the quantity chosen offers the greatest convenience in the calculation to be made. A basis of 1 lb of C would not seem to be so convenient as 1 mole of C, which is readily associated with quantities expressed in the equation for the reaction. In the present example, a basis of 100 moles of flue gas would appear to be a good basis on which to work. In any case, the basis chosen should be clearly stated and then followed consistently until notice is given of a change of basis.

If 100 moles of flue gas are used as a basis, the following calculations can be made:

Carbon burned = moles of CO_2 formed = 14.2 moles or (14.2)(12) = 170.4 lb

Carbon dioxide produced = 14.2 moles or (14.2)(44) = 625 lb or (14.2)(359) = 5100 ft³ when measured at 32°F and 1 atm

Oxygen used in reaction = 14.2 moles or (14.2)(32) = 455 lb

Oxygen in excess of amount required for combustion in accordance with the equation (stoichiometric requirement) = 6.7 moles

Excess air beyond stoichiometric requirement = (6.7)(100/20.9) = 32.1 moles

Required air = (14.2)(100/20.9) = 67.9 moles

Total air admitted = 32.1 + 67.9 or [(79.1)(100/79.1)] = 100 moles

These and other quantities which could be calculated depend in magnitude upon the basis chosen. From them the following quantities can be obtained which are independent of the arbitrarily chosen basis:

Oxygen required per pound of C burned = 455/170.4 or $\frac{32}{12}$ = 2.67 lb

Carbon dioxide produced per pound of C burned = 5100/170.4 = 29.9 ft^3 at standard conditions

Excess air as percentage of required air = (32.1/67.9)(100%) or (6.7/14.2)(100%) = 47.2%

Percentage of the air admitted which was required = (67.9/100) (100%) or (14.2/20.9)(100%) = 67.9%

Flue-gas analysis if no excess air had been admitted but combustion had still been complete: 20.9% CO_2 and 79.1% N_2

In many cases water vapor is present in gases. There are many possibilities during sampling procedures and subsequent handling of the gas sample for changes to occur in the amount of water vapor present. For example, if the temperature of a moist flue gas is lowered, water vapor might condense out. Sometimes samples are collected over water and thus become saturated with water vapor although they might originally have been dry. For reasons such as these it is customary to make gas analyses, and to report gas compositions, on a dry basis, determining and reporting water vapor content separately when this information is required.

When a fuel gas, such as methane (CH_4), which is the major component of natural gas, is burned, the hydrogen burns to water vapor which, as stated above, does not appear in the analysis of the combustion gases. This does not mean that the presence of water vapor can be ignored. The combustion reaction for methane is

$$CH_4(g) + 2O_2(g) \rightarrow CO_2(g) + 2H_2O(g)$$

There will also be N_2 present in the flue gases because the oxygen is ordinarily obtained by use of air. Let us suppose that this reaction is carried to completion as written, without use of any excess oxygen. If we choose 1 mole of CH_4 as a basis, 2 moles of O_2 will be required. If the O_2 comes from air, there will be (2)(79.1/20.9) = 7.57 moles of N_2 brought in, and it will remain unchanged in the process. There will be 1 mole of CO_2 produced, and it will appear in the flue gas. At the same time 2 moles of H_2O will be produced, and although it is present in the flue gas it will not appear in the analysis. The flue gas as shown in the analysis will consist of 1 mole of CO_2 and 7.57 moles of N_2, and its analysis will show (1/8.57)(100%) = 11.7% CO_2 and

$(7.57/8.57)(100\%) = 88.3\%$ N_2. If the volume of flue gases at 500°F and 1 atm is to be calculated, the presence of the water vapor, although not shown in the analysis, is important and the required volume, on the basis chosen above, would be

$$(1 + 2 + 7.57)(359)(460 + 500)/(460 + 32) = 7400 \text{ ft}^3$$

If the combustion of a hydrocarbon fuel in air resulted in a flue-gas analysis of 13.9% CO_2, 0.7% CO, 3.7% O_2, and 81.7% N_2, it is possible to deduce a number of facts from this information alone. Although excess air is provided, inspection of the analysis shows that the combustion has not been complete. This is a common occurrence in industrial furnaces, and it may result from lack of adequate contact between oxygen and combustible matter in the furnace, or from the gases being cooled below reacting temperature before combustion is completed. The fact that the percentage of N_2 in the analysis exceeds 79.1% points to the probability that some oxygen which came in with the air no longer appears in the analysis and that water vapor has probably been formed.

As a working basis for calculations, let us choose 100 moles of flue gas of the composition shown by the analysis given above. It may be assumed that the N_2 of the entering air remains inert and that all of it appears in the flue gas. A material which passes unchanged through a process is very helpful in calculations and is called a *tracer*. The O_2 brought in from the air with the N_2 shown is $(81.7)(20.9/79.1) = 21.6$ moles. Of this,

$$13.9 + 0.7/2 + 3.7 = 17.95 \text{ moles}$$

is accounted for in the analysis and $21.6 - 17.95 = 3.65$ moles has disappeared, presumably being in the form of H_2O. For each mole of O_2 going to form H_2O there will be 4 moles of H. The hydrogen obtained from the fuel is $(4)(3.65) = 14.6$ moles of H. The carbon in the fuel, assuming that it is all burned to either CO or CO_2, is $13.9 + 0.7 = 14.6$ moles of C. The weights of H and C, respectively, are $(14.6)(1.008) = 14.7$ lb and $(14.6)(12) = 175.2$ lb. With solids and liquids, analyses are reported in weight percentage, and the analysis of the fuel would be $(175.2)(100\%)/(175.2 + 14.7) = 92.3\%$ C, the remainder being 7.7% H. The fuel is predominantly carbon by weight, although its empirical formula would be $(CH)_x$.

The volume of flue gas produced per pound of fuel, if measured at 300°F and 14.5 psia, would be

$$\left[\frac{100 + (14.6/2)}{14.7 + 175.2}\right] (359) \left(\frac{460 + 300}{460 + 32}\right) \left(\frac{14.7}{14.5}\right) = 318 \text{ ft}^3$$

The H_2O produced in the combustion is included because under the conditions specified it would not condense out.

The excess O_2 beyond that required stoichiometrically for complete combustion would be $3.7 - 0.7/2 = 3.35$ moles. The required O_2 for complete combustion would be

$$13.9 + 0.7/2 + 3.65 = 17.9 \text{ moles}$$

The excess air furnished is then $(3.35/17.9)(100\%) = 18.7\%$ of the required air. If complete combustion could be obtained without use of excess air, the components of the flue gas would be 14.6 moles of CO_2, $(2)(3.65) = 7.3$ moles of H_2O, and

$$(14.6 + 3.65)(79.1/20.9) = 69.1 \text{ moles of } N_2$$

making a total of 83.7 moles of *dry* flue gas. The analysis would then be $(14.6/83.7)(100\%) = 17.4\%$ CO_2 and

$$(69.1/83.7)(100\%) = 82.6\% \text{ } N_2$$

The discussion of specific cases of interpretation of the behavior of gases has centered around the combustion process, but the principles and procedures apply as well to other chemical and physical processes in which gases are involved.

Deviations from Perfect-gas Behavior

For gases at high pressures, the simple laws fail to give accurate predictions of behavior, and either more complicated prediction methods or experimental data must be relied upon. For example, at 100°F and 100 psia the perfect-gas predictions of volume are higher than the actual volumes for the following gases by the percentages indicated: N_2, 0.01%; CH_4, 1.2%; CO_2, 3.2%; and H_2S, 5.0%. The deviation of steam from perfect-gas behavior is illustrated in Fig. 4-1. Under some conditions the volume as predicted by the perfect-gas laws will differ from the actual volume by several hundred per cent. Deviations of 10% or more are frequently encountered in industrial operation. For this reason it is desirable to use experimentally determined results whenever they are available and to rely upon the gas laws when

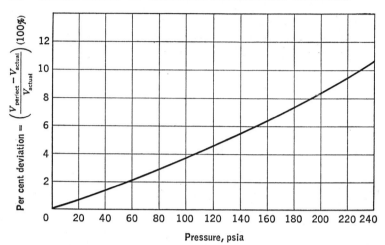

FIG. 4-1. Deviation from perfect-gas behavior for steam at 400°F.

no other information is at hand or when favorable conditions of low pressure, high temperature, and remoteness from condensation prevail.

5

Material Balances

Many industrial operations can be carried out in either of two
ways which may be called batch and continuous operations.
These two methods can be exemplified for the simple case of
heating a solution with steam, as shown in Fig. 5-1. In the *batch
process* the solution, at its original temperature, is run into a tank
or kettle, and it is then heated as a batch by admission of steam
to a surrounding jacket or to internal coils. When the tankful
of solution has reached the desired temperature, it is withdrawn,
a new batch of cool solution is added, and the process is repeated.
In the *continuous process* the solution can be passed slowly but
continuously through a pipe coil which is surrounded by a steam
jacket, the heating area and the rate of flow being adjusted so
that the solution leaves the outlet end of the coil at the desired
temperature.

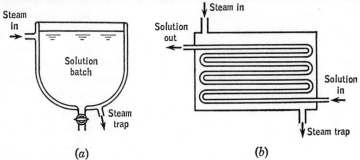

FIG. 5-1. Heating of solution by (*a*) batch operation and (*b*) continuous
operation.

Batch Processes

Each of these procedures has certain typical advantages in its favor, and the choice of which one should be used in a given case is a responsibility of the engineer. The batch-process equipment can usually be assembled from more readily available parts or general plant equipment. It does not require such close control as the continuous process, and that control is needed only near the end of the heating operation. It does, however, require more supervision in admitting cold solution and withdrawing heated solution from the tank. The batch process is intermittent in that it only accepts cool solution at intervals and supplies heated solution also at intervals. If other steps in the process before or after this one are continuous in nature, some sort of storage facilities must be provided to absorb the fluctuations of material movement caused by the batch-operated heating step. If the tank is an open one, the pressure on the solution must be brought to that of the atmosphere, and this may mean loss of pressure and extra pumping if the other steps are carried on at higher pressures.

Continuous Processes

The continuous process, although requiring more carefully designed equipment than the batch process, can ordinarily be handled in less space, fits in with other continuous steps more smoothly, and can be conducted at any prevailing pressure without release to atmospheric pressure. The temperature of each part of the equipment remains substantially constant during operation, thus avoiding the fluctuations which are unavoidable with the batch procedure.

Continuous operation of processes has many advantages and is ordinarily a goal in engineering design. There are occasions, however, when batch operation can be used to advantage. It is difficult to conduct certain operations on a continuous basis, and if there is one necessary batch step in a sequence of steps, it may be more advantageous to have other batch steps synchronized with it than to intermix batch and continuous steps. Batch operations are frequently found in experimental and pilot-plant operations and may, at a later stage of process development, be converted to continuous steps.

Steady-state Processes

In a strictly steady process, conditions at any one place in the system hold constant and do not change with respect to time. Conditions will be different at different points in the system but remain constant at each particular point.   This is called a steady-state process and is in many respects an ideal one.   In most operations there will be small or large fluctuations in conditions. In the continuous solution heater discussed above, the steam pressure in the heating jacket may vary somewhat with respect to time and thus will affect the rate of heat transfer and consequently the temperature of the solution at any point in the coil. The solution may be fed to the heater from a pump, and there may be some pulsations in the operation of the pump which cause variations in the pressure at a given point in the equipment. These are examples of the numerous factors which can cause deviations from steady-state operation.   These disturbances, however, are often minor in their influence upon the operation and in that case can be overlooked.

For quantitative consideration, the steady-state process offers certain advantages of simplicity.   Irregular, and even periodic, fluctuations are complex, and their treatment mathematically becomes difficult and arduous.   This fact offers a strong incentive to assume steady-state operation in mathematical or quantitative treatment for the sake of greater simplicity.   Fortunately, in many actual operations the fluctuations are small, and their effect upon over-all conditions is small.   In these cases, treatment of the problems on a steady-state basis is justified and convenient.

Continuity Principle in Steady-state Processes

Consider the simple example of the steady-state flow of a gas through a pipeline at constant temperature.   The pressure and the velocity of flow at any point along the length of the line will be constant with respect to time, although the pressure is likely to decrease somewhat from point to point in the direction of flow. At some point A in the pipeline, the pressure, temperature, and velocity of flow will be constant.   From this it follows that the quantity of material passing section A in a given interval of time also remains constant.   The same deductions can be made regarding any other section B.   If more material passed in through section A in any unit time interval than passed out through section B, there would be an accumulation of material occurring between the two sections, and this would cause a change of conditions there as time went on. Because this situation would be inconsistent with steady state, it follows that, if steady-state conditions prevail, there can be no such difference in the amounts of material passing sections A and B, or, in fact, any other section in the flowing stream. An important relationship characteristic of steady flow is, then, that the same amount of material passes each section of the flowing stream in any given time interval. It is applicable to both simple and complex processes as long as steady-state conditions are in effect. It holds true not only for the whole stream but for any constituent of the stream which passes through the system unchanged in amount during transit.

The continuity relationship simplifies the material balance in the analysis of steady-flow processes. Consider the case of the gas flowing through the pipeline discussed above. Let us say that this gas consists of a mixture of CO and O_2 in the proportion of 1 mole of CO to 2 moles of O_2. If no reaction occurs between sections A and B, the same proportion exists at each intermediate section, and the amount of each of the two constituents passing each section will be the same, and constant with respect to time. If reaction between the CO and the O_2 occurs, however, the situation will be different. During reaction, CO and O_2 will decrease, and CO_2 will appear and increase in proportion as the gas proceeds along the pipeline. It is obvious that the amount of CO passing out of section B will no longer be equal to that entering through section A per unit of time. This process can, nevertheless, be carried out on a steady-state basis because, once the operation has become stabilized, the conditions existing at any given section will be constant with respect to time, even though conditions are different from point to point.

Although the amounts of CO, O_2, and CO_2 change from point to point during flow, the total amounts of C and O present in the mixture do not vary, and so they offer a satisfactory basis for a material balance. One can then say that the amount of carbon passing each section per second is constant and the same, whether combined in the form of CO or CO_2. Similarly, the amount of oxygen is the same for each section, whether in the form of O_2, CO, or CO_2. If 1 mole of CO passes section A per minute, in the mixture discussed above, and no CO remains when section B is reached, it follows that 1 mole of CO_2 and 1.5 moles of O_2 pass section B per minute. At some intermediate section at which one-half of the original CO had been oxidized the rates of passage of materials would have been 0.5 mole of CO, 1.75 moles of O_2, and 0.5 mole of CO_2 per minute, the rates of passage of carbon and oxygen being constant throughout, at 1 mole of C and 5 moles of O per minute, without regard to state of combination.

Material Balance for Steady-state Process

A somewhat more complicated example will serve to show more effectively the utility of the material balance for steady-state operation. In a continuous process, H_2 and Cl_2 gases are fed into a reaction chamber where they combine to form HCl gas which then passes to an absorber and is there absorbed in water to form aqueous hydrochloric acid. Chlorine gas is fed to the system at the rate of 1 ton/hr with a 20% excess of hydrogen gas over that stoichiometrically required for reaction. It will be assumed that all the HCl gas produced is absorbed and that the resulting acid is 25 wt % HCl. From these data a number of facts can be ascertained about this process.

The reaction occurring is $H_2 + Cl_2 \rightarrow 2HCl$, and 1 ton of chlorine per hour is equal to $(1)(2000)/(2)(35.46) = 28.2$ moles of Cl_2 per hour, which corresponds to $(2)(28.2) = 56.4$ moles of HCl if all of the chlorine is used up in the reaction, which will be assumed because an excess of hydrogen gas is provided. It should be emphasized that this is an *assumption* made for lack of more explicit information and is not necessarily a fact. The assumption, however, permits the calculation to proceed. The hydrogen required stoichiometrically to react with the chlorine is 28.2 moles of H_2 per hour, the amount admitted is

$$(1.20)(28.2) = 33.8 \text{ moles of } H_2 \text{ per hour}$$

and the amount unused in the reaction, according to the assumption made, is 5.6 moles of H_2 per hour. This last fact follows essentially from a material balance for H between that entering in a given time and that leaving during the same period under conditions of steady-state operation. A similar balance for HCl in the absorber can be used. HCl enters as gas at the rate of 56.4 moles/hr and leaves only as solution, and so the HCl in the outlet solution must be the same in amount per unit of time and equal to 56.4 moles/hr, or $(56.4)(36.5) = 2057$ lb/hr. Because this amount of HCl is 25% of the acid solution produced from it, the weight of acid is $(2057)(\frac{100}{25}) = 8230$ lb/hr, and the amount of water leaving with the acid is 6173 lb/hr. This must also be the rate at which water is added to the system.

In arriving at these figures several material balances have been used: namely, that for Cl in the reactor, that for H in the reactor, that for HCl in the absorber, and that for water in the absorber. As an over-all check on the calculations we can say that for steady-state operation the summation of the weights of all materials entering must equal the summation of all those leaving in a given time period. Then, on the basis of an hour of operation, the weight of H_2 gas entering + the weight of Cl_2 gas entering + the weight of water entering must equal the weight of excess H_2 gas leaving + the weight of acid solution leaving. Quantitatively, $(33.8)(2.016) + 2000 + 6180$ should equal $(5.6)(2.016) + 8230$, or 8241 should equal 8241.

Example 5-A. In many cases of continuous processes met in industry there are several streams of material entering and several leaving. Material balance calculations can be useful in such situations. An example of these calculations is offered in the process step of concentrating nitric acid. When nitric acid is produced by oxidizing gaseous ammonia to form NO, and then NO_2, the latter must be brought into contact with water to form nitric acid. The resulting acid contains 50 to 60 wt % HNO_3, but it is too dilute for a number of industrial applications. If this solution is evaporated, water vapor will be formed, and thus some concentration of the acid can be accomplished. When the concentration reaches approximately 68% HNO_3, the whole solution vaporizes without change of composition, and so any further concentration by simple evaporation is not possible. In order to overcome this difficulty, investigation showed that if an agent is added which will serve to decrease considerably the partial pressure of water vapor from the mixture, concentrated nitric acid can be distilled from it. Sulfuric acid has been used for this purpose for many years. More recently, however, it has been proposed to use a solution of $Mg(NO_3)_2$ instead. A flow sheet for the process is shown in Fig. 5-A1, giving the steps of the process and concentrations of solutions involved.†

It is desired to determine for this process, on the basis of 1000 lb of concentrated nitric acid produced:

1. The weight of dilute acid fed to the system
2. The weight of $Mg(NO_3)_2$ which is circulated in solution
3. The weight of water vapor leaving the evaporator

† *Hercules Chemist*, no. 34 (October, 1958).

The desired quantities can be obtained by making suitable material balances. Many different balances can be set up in connection with this process. For example, there are total weight, HNO_3, and water balances applying to the entire system as a unit; there are similar balances for the distillation unit alone; and also there are balances for the evaporator alone. In fact, balances can be set up for each point in the system at which streams merge or separate. Not all these balances are independent of each other, and some of them are not particularly helpful

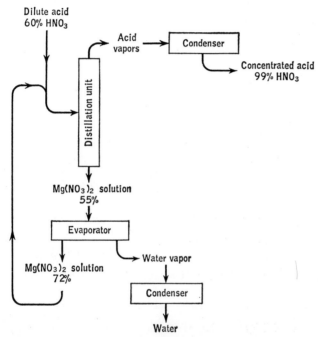

FIG. 5-A1. Process for concentrating nitric acid.

for a given calculation. The first step, then, is to choose those balances which seem to offer promise of giving the results desired, and then formulate them quantitatively.

In order to evaluate the relation between weights of concentrated acid, dilute acid, and water, balances for the system as a whole would seem to offer the most help. These can be stated as follows:

Total weight balance (basis of 1000 lb of concentrated acid):

$$\text{Dilute acid} = \text{conc. acid} + \text{vapor formed}$$
$$x \text{ lb} = 1000 \text{ lb} + z \text{ lb}$$

HNO₃ balance (for whole system, on the same basis):

$$\text{Dilute acid} = \text{conc. acid} + \text{vapor formed}$$
$$0.60x = (0.99)(1000) + 0$$

From this balance,

$$x = (0.99/0.60)(1000) = 1650 \text{ lb of dilute acid fed}$$

From the first balance,

$$z = x - 1000 = 1650 - 1000 = 650 \text{ lb of water condensed}$$

These results may be tested by use in a third balance, as follows:

Water balance:
$$\text{Dilute acid} = \text{conc. acid} + \text{vapor formed}$$
$$(0.40)(1650) = (0.01)(1000) + 650$$
$$660 = 10 + 650 = 660$$

The balance proves to be consistent on the basis of the results as found.

In order to find the weight of $Mg(NO_3)_2$ circulated, the distillation unit offers promise, taking into account the $Mg(NO_3)_2$ solution added to the feed stream, and letting y be the weight of $Mg(NO_3)_2$.

Total weight balance (basis of 1000 lb of concentrated acid):

Conc. $Mg(NO_3)_2$ soln. + dilute acid

$$= \text{conc. acid} + \text{dilute } Mg(NO_3)_2 \text{ soln.}$$

$$\left(\frac{1.00}{0.72}\right) y + 1650 = 1000 + \left(\frac{1.00}{0.55}\right) y$$

Solving, $\quad y(1.819 - 1.389) = 1650 - 1000 \text{ or } y = \dfrac{650}{0.43} = 1511 \text{ lb}$

Again, an additional balance can be used to test the result. This balance will be applied to the evaporator unit.

Water balance (basis of 1000 lb of concentrated acid):

$$\text{Dilute } Mg(NO_3)_2 \text{ soln.} = \text{conc. } Mg(NO_3)_2 \text{ soln.} + \text{vapor formed}$$
$$\left(\frac{0.45}{0.55}\right)(1511) = \left(\frac{0.28}{0.72}\right)(1511) + 650$$
$$1237 = 587 + 650 = 1237$$

The results desired for 1000 lb of concentrated acid produced are

1650 lb of dilute acid fed to the system
1511 lb of $Mg(NO_3)_2$ in the solution circulated
650 lb of water vapor leaving the evaporator

Non-steady-state Processes

Although the idea of steady state finds major application in the establishment of material balances in chemical processes, the concept of the non-steady state must also be given consideration. Actually the steady state is a special case of the non-steady state so that a study of the latter situation gives the general approach to a problem and merits a brief discussion here.

When the state is not steady, the conditions at a point vary with respect to time, in contrast to the steady-state operation in which the point conditions are invariant with time. The often-used statement

$$\text{Input} - \text{output} = \text{accumulation}$$

is the best starting point for analysis of a material balance in a non-steady-state situation. For steady state, the accumulation term is zero, and so the input equals the output. In a non-steady state, however, there is accumulation, which may be either positive or negative in sign, and it adds complexity to the mathematical expression for the material balance, as compared to the more simple algebraic forms found for steady-state cases.

Example 5-B. An example can best describe the material balance for the non-steady-state case. Consider the problem in which methane is to be flushed from a storage tank by means of nitrogen. For a tank volume of 100 ft^3 and a nitrogen flow rate of 30 ft^3/min, determine the time required to reach a gas composition of 5 vol % methane in the tank when the process is carried out at atmospheric pressure and 70°F, and the tank was originally filled with methane. Assume for this problem that perfect mixing of the gases in the tank is realized at all times. The problem can be analyzed by consideration of the system during a differential period of time $d\theta$, during which conditions may be taken as essentially constant. Then, if C is the concentration of nitrogen in moles/ft^3,

$$\text{Input of nitrogen} = \left(\frac{30}{359}\right)\left(\frac{460 + 32}{460 + 70}\right)(d\theta) = 0.0776\, d\theta \text{ moles}$$

$$\text{Output of nitrogen} = (C)(30)(d\theta) \text{ moles}$$
$$\text{Accumulation of nitrogen} = 100\, dC \text{ moles}$$

in which dC is the change in C in the time $d\theta$. Incorporation of these quantities in the above equation gives

$$0.0776\, d\theta - 30C\, d\theta = 100\, dC$$

or

$$\frac{100\, dC}{0.0776 - 30C} = d\theta$$

then, by integration,

$$\frac{-100}{30} \ln (0.0776 - 30C) \Big|_{C_1}^{C_2} = \theta_2 - \theta_1$$

in which C_1 is zero when θ_1 is zero. The problem is to find θ_2 when

$$C_2 = (0.95) \left(\frac{1}{359}\right) \left(\frac{460 + 32}{460 + 70}\right) = 0.00246 \text{ moles/ft}^3$$

By substitution in the above equation there results

$$\theta_2 = \frac{100}{30} \ln \frac{0.0776}{0.0776 - (30)(0.00246)} = 10.1 \text{ min}$$

All non-steady-state analyses yield differential equations because of the need for analyzing the problem on the basis of an infinitesimal or very short time period during which the state may be considered to be substantially constant. The differential equations thus obtained are not all readily solved. In the special steady-state case the system is fixed in character regardless of the time period considered.

6

Energy

Energy is required in the operation of a chemical plant. Its source may be hydroelectric, solar, or fuels such as coal, gas, wood, and petroleum. Today the use of fissionable materials which give energy as a result of nuclear reactions is becoming more practical, and soon nuclear fusion reactions will probably contribute to our energy supply. Regardless of the source of energy, the engineer must know the fundamental principles in the treatment of energy changes in plant operations. The reason is found in economics, because, whatever the energy source, charges are made for its use. Charges can result from fuel consumption as well as from amortization of capital expenditures made for equipment in which the energy changes occur. If the engineer had no rational way of dealing with energy changes, he would not be in a position to minimize the annual energy charges to his plant. The rational way is provided by thermodynamics—a systematized study of energy changes. Of special interest are the internal energy, the enthalpy, heats of reaction, and heats of combustion.

Internal Energy

Internal energy is the measure of the *intrinsic energy* of the particular body of matter, or system, under consideration. It is often designated by the letter E, and in the most general case its component parts may be summarized as follows:

$$E = E_{\text{translation}} + E_{\text{external rotation}} + E_{\text{internal rotation}} + E_{\text{vibration}}$$
$$+ E_{\text{interaction}} + E_{\text{electronic configuration}} \quad (6\text{-}1)$$

59

Thus it represents a summation of the energies of the molecules without regard to the velocity of the system in space or its position in a potential field such as that of gravity. It cannot be evaluated on an absolute basis, but fortunately that is not necessary because differences in the quantity are sufficient. It is convenient, however, to tabulate values of E for different states so that differences can be easily ascertained for any given change in state. This objective can be accomplished by choosing arbitrarily a value of E, perhaps 0 or 1, for some convenient state and then basing values of E at all other states on this datum or reference value, using the measured values of ΔE. This procedure is analogous to our practice of basing altitudes upon mean sea level as a datum elevation. The resulting set of values of E has no meaning in an absolute sense, but is completely satisfactory so long as only values of ΔE are needed in application of the information.

The internal energy of a system which is at equilibrium within itself is characteristic of the state of the system. It has the same value every time the system returns to a given state, no matter how it reaches that state. For example, a sample of gas at a specified temperature and pressure will have a certain value of its internal energy. Both its temperature and pressure can be changed arbitrarily, but, if the sample is returned to the original state again, it will have the same internal energy that it did before. The internal energy is, therefore, a property of the system. It is an extensive property because it depends not only on the composition of the system and its state but also on the amount of material in the system. In other words, the internal energy depends on the number and kinds of molecules present, their translational energy levels, their rotational energies, etc.

If a means is available for treating the mechanics of the grouping of molecules, then changes in internal energy can be evaluated from an understanding of the kinetic and potential relationships. Statistical and quantum mechanics allow that analysis for gases at low pressure when spectroscopic data are available. In the usual case, changes in internal energy are evaluated experimentally.

Change in Internal Energy

The internal energy of a system will be affected if energy is transferred to it or from it in relation to its surroundings. Energy can be transferred from the surroundings to a system, or the reverse, in a variety of ways. One way is by the action of a force through a distance in changing the volume of the system. Such a mechanical transfer of energy is called *work* and is given the symbol W. Its sign is arbitrarily taken as positive when energy is transferred by this means from the system *to* the surroundings, and as negative for the reverse process.

Another way by which energy can be transferred to or from the system is as the result of a difference in temperature between the surroundings and the system. Energy transferred in this manner is called *heat, Q*. Its sign follows just the opposite of the convention used for work; namely, it is positive when energy is added to the system *from* the surroundings.

The quantity called work is often considered to include other energy transfers than those that affect the volume of the system. Noteworthy among these is the addition or withdrawal of energy by electrical means, as in electrolysis or the action of a battery, respectively.

Both heat and work consist of energy being transferred to or from the surroundings and are measurable in the surroundings rather than in the system. They are in no way characteristic of the system or its state, but depend only on the process that the system is undergoing. Their values depend on the exact way in which the energy transfer is accomplished, and they are said, therefore, to be *functions* of the process, or its "path."

If the methods of transfer of energy to or from the system are limited to heat and work, they represent the only ways by which the internal energy of a system of fixed weight can be modified. On this basis, the increase in internal energy of the system can be equated to the energy transferred to the system thermally, Q, plus the energy transferred to it mechanically, $-W$. This may be expressed in equation form as

$$\Delta E = Q - W \qquad (6\text{-}2)$$

This relation is known in thermodynamics as the "first law" equation. As stated above, it applies to a system of fixed weight, called a *closed system* because no material is transferred across its boundary. *Open systems*, which will be discussed briefly later, have material transferred across their boundaries.

Example 6-A. A suspension of a finely divided solid substance in water is being held in a large tank pending further processing. Unless the slurry is continuously stirred, the solid settles out and cakes in

the bottom of the tank.   The necessary agitation is provided by a pro-
peller-type stirrer with a power input to the shaft of 1 hp.   If the temperature and volume of the slurry remain constant, how much energy,
expressed in Btu, is being transferred thermally from the slurry to the
surroundings per hour of operation?

Solution.   Under the conditions described, with no energy effects
from reaction or physical combination of components, the internal
energy of the slurry will remain constant.   Equation (6-2) may then
be written

$$\Delta E = 0 = Q - W$$

or

$$Q = W$$

In the mixing process, energy is being transferred mechanically from
the surroundings to the system.   If there are no bearing losses, the
input of energy to the stirrer shaft is equal to the energy used in mixing.
This energy input by action of a force through a distance will be considered in this case to be work, although it does not result in a change in
volume of the system.

Then, on a basis of 1 hr of operation,

$$Q = W = - \text{ (1 hp) (1 hr)} \left(25\overset{*}{4}4 \; \frac{\text{Btu}}{\text{hp-hr}} \right) = -2544 \text{ Btu}$$

This value for the thermal transfer Q of energy *to* the system is negative,
indicating that the transfer in this case is from the system to the
surroundings.

Intensive and Extensive Properties

Intensive properties of a system are those properties which are
characteristic of it without regard to the amount of material
present in the system.   Examples of such properties are pressure,
temperature, density, and viscosity.   Each of these properties
can be the same for either a large or a small sample of a given
material.

Values of extensive properties, on the other hand, depend not
only on the kind of material and its state, but also on the amount
of it in the system.   Internal energy and volume are examples
of extensive properties.   It should be remembered that Q and W,
although extensive in character, are not properties of the system.

Enthalpy

In working with energy quantities, a certain combination of
properties appears frequently enough so that, for the sake of

brevity, it is convenient to give it a name and a symbol. The combination is the sum of the internal energy and the product of the pressure and the volume of the system. Because it is composed entirely of quantities that are properties of the system and are characteristic of the system at any given state, the combination quantity is also characteristic of the system at that state and is a property. This property is called *enthalpy* and is given the symbol H. Its definition can be stated in equation form as

$$H = E + PV \qquad (6\text{-}3)$$

Because both E and V are extensive properties, it follows that the value of H for a given material at a given state depends on the amount of material present, and enthalpy is an extensive property. Its utility will be seen as the discussion develops. As stated earlier in this chapter, values of E are tabulated on the basis of an arbitrary datum state. Because the value of H depends on the value of E, it is also based on the same arbitrary datum. Fortunately, as with E, values of H are used primarily to ascertain differences, and so no difficulty results from this dependence.

If Eqs. (6-2) and (6-3) are combined, there results

$$\Delta H = Q - W + \Delta(PV) \qquad (6\text{-}4)$$

For a state change at constant pressure, Eq. (6-4) gives

$$\Delta H = Q - W + P\,\Delta V \qquad (6\text{-}5)$$

Then, if the work W is expansion work only and the process is conducted without friction, W is equal to $P\,\Delta V$. Equation (6-5) becomes

$$\Delta H = Q \qquad (6\text{-}6)$$

For this particular situation, then, the energy transfer to the system as a result of a temperature gradient is equal to the enthalpy change for the system. Because frictionless processes at constant pressure are frequently dealt with in chemical engineering calculations, Eq. (6-6) is an important one, and the convenience in the use of the concept of enthalpy may be seen.

In using enthalpy, it is necessary to remember that it, like the internal energy E, depends in value, for a given system of fixed weight, only on the state of the system. For this reason, the value of ΔH between any two given states is independent of the path followed by the system in passing from the initial to the final state. The value of ΔH will be the same for all processes beginning and ending at these given states.

Change in Internal Energy during Chemical Reaction

Consider a system which consists, for example, of a mixture of two gases which are capable of reacting with each other to form a third gas. The original gas mixture is to be confined in a container with rigid walls, which are completely insulating against thermal transfer. It is desired to know what change in internal energy of the system occurs if the two gases are allowed to react under these special conditions. Referring to Eq. (6-2), it is seen that ΔE can be ascertained in terms of Q and W. Because the boundary of the system is not movable, there will be no change in the volume of the system, and so $W = 0$. Because the walls are completely insulating, $Q = 0$. It is seen, therefore, that under these conditions the internal energy of the system has not changed, although many changes have taken place within the boundaries of the system. Many of the original molecules will have disappeared, with new ones forming. The temperature and pressure will undoubtedly have changed. In other words, the state of the system has changed markedly, but Eq. (6-2) shows that the system at the original and final states will have the same internal energy. This situation results from the fact that internal energy is affected only by Q and W, and, if these exchanges with the surroundings are precluded, internal energy remains constant during changes that may occur within the boundary of the system.

It is of interest to note, for the process considered above, that although ΔE is equal to zero, the same is not likely to be true for ΔH. According to Eq. (6-4), when $\Delta E = 0$, ΔH becomes equal to $\Delta(PV)$. Although V is kept constant, it is highly probable that the reaction will involve changes both in the number of moles of gas and in the temperature existing. These factors will change the pressure, and so $\Delta(PV)$ will not be equal to zero, and ΔH will not equal zero.

Processes involving chemical reactions are seldom performed under the special conditions set for the example discussed above. In most instances the processes involve either heat or work or both, and so there are likely to be changes in the internal energy of the system. The point to be remembered here is that internal energy is affected only by interchanges with the surroundings and not by changes occurring completely within the system.

Internal Energy and Enthalpy of Perfect Gases

The defining equation for perfect gases, $PV = \mathbf{n}\mathbf{R}T$, shows through thermodynamics that the internal energy for such gases is a function of the temperature, but is independent of the pressure or of their specific volumes. This fact makes relatively simple the calculation of the internal energy change of a perfect gas with change in temperature. The process can be carried out by any convenient path which accomplishes the desired temperature change and for which ΔE can be calculated. It does not matter for this purpose whether P or V changes or does not change during this process.

From Eq. (6-2), $\Delta E = Q - W$, it can be seen that, if $W = 0$, ΔE can be obtained by evaluation only of Q. Such a process would have no change in volume and would be called "isochoric." The heat for an isochoric process is equal to the heat capacity at constant volume multiplied by the change in temperature. This relationship can be expressed in the following general differential form:

$$dE = C_V \, dT \qquad (6\text{-}7)$$

Because the heat capacity of a perfect gas is a function only of the temperature, this equation can be integrated simply, if the relation between C_V and T is known for any pressure, to give the equation

$$\Delta E = \int_{T_A}^{T_B} C_V \, dT \qquad (6\text{-}8)$$

For real substances, this equation gives the change in internal energy between two states which are at the same volume. For perfect gases, however, it can be used to evaluate ΔE for any two states because for such gases C_V is independent of pressure. If the temperature range involved is not great and an arithmetic average value of C_V can be used as a constant, Eq. (6-8) simplifies to

$$\Delta E \approx C_{V_{av}} \Delta T \qquad (6\text{-}9)$$

The change of enthalpy from state A to state B, in accordance with Eq. (6-3), would be

$$\Delta H = H_B - H_A = E_B + P_B V_B - E_A - P_A V_A = \Delta E + \Delta(PV)$$
$$(6\text{-}10)$$

For a perfect gas, the product PV is a function of temperature but is independent of the particular pressure P (or volume V) at which the system exists. Because the same is true of E, it follows that $\Delta E + \Delta(PV)$, or ΔH, is a function only of the temperature involved in the case of a perfect gas. It should perhaps be emphasized that this characteristic of E and H for perfect gases does not apply to real gases which deviate from perfect-gas behavior. The values of E and H for real gases can vary markedly with pressure at a given temperature, because for such gases C_P and C_V are functions of pressure as well as temperature. Experimental determinations of heat capacities at various pressures are necessary in these instances.

In order to evaluate dH for a perfect gas, Eq. (6-3) can be differentiated, the differential form of Eq. (6-8) substituted, and the perfect-gas equation applied. These procedures give

$$dH = dE + d(PV) = C_V \, dT + \mathbf{R} \, dT = (C_V + \mathbf{R}) \, dT \quad (6\text{-}11)$$

But for a perfect gas $(C_V + \mathbf{R})$ is equal to C_P, the heat capacity at constant pressure, and so it develops that

$$dH = C_P \, dT \tag{6-12}$$

and

$$\Delta H = \int_{T_A}^{T_B} C_P \, dT \approx C_{P_{av}} \Delta T \tag{6-13}$$

These equations above were developed for perfect gases and give values of dH and ΔH, respectively, for any changes of state, because C_P for a perfect gas is independent of either pressure or volume. The same equations will apply, however, for any substance when limited to the special case of a change of state carried out at constant pressure. This can be seen from Eq. (6-6) because, for an isobaric process, Q is equal to $\int C_P \, dT$.

Example 6-B. A vessel contains 0.25 lb of CO_2 at 77°F and atmospheric pressure. How much energy would be required from the surroundings to raise the temperature of the CO_2 to 250°F while keeping the pressure constant?

Solution. At constant pressure for a closed system

$$Q = \Delta H = \int_{T_1}^{T_2} C_P \, dT$$

The molal heat capacity for carbon dioxide as a function of temperature may be written as[†]

$$C_P = 7.70 + 0.0053T - 0.00000083T^2$$

when T is the temperature in degrees Kelvin.

$$t_1 = 77°F = 25°C = 298.2°K$$
$$t_2 = 250°F = 121.1°C = 394.3°K$$

For 1 g mole of CO_2,

$$Q = \int_{298.2}^{394.3} (7.70 + 0.0053T - 0.00000083T^2) \, dT$$
$$Q = 740.0 + 176.4 - 9.6$$
$$Q = 906.8 \text{ cal/g mole}$$

For 0.25/44 lb mole,

$$Q = (0.25/44)(906.8)\overset{*}{(1.8)} = 9.3 \text{ Btu}$$

Heat of Reaction

Heat of reaction is the energy required by thermal transfer from the surroundings by a system reacting while kept at constant temperature and pressure. Under these conditions the heat of reaction is equal to ΔH. For example, in the reaction

$$SO_2(g) + \tfrac{1}{2}O_2(g) \rightarrow SO_3(g) \tag{6-14}$$

the heat of reaction at 25°C and a pressure of 1 atm is $-23,450$ cal/mole of SO_3 formed, the minus sign being used because in this case energy is transferred to the surroundings for the process at constant temperature and pressure. The equation is often written as follows:

$$SO_2(g) + \tfrac{1}{2}O_2(g) \rightarrow SO_3(g) \qquad Q = \Delta H_{25°C} = -23,450 \tag{6-15}$$

The subscript 25°C represents the temperature at which the reaction takes place. When there is no explicit statement, the

[†] W. H. Walker, W. K. Lewis, W. H. McAdams, and E. R. Gilliland, "Principles of Chemical Engineering," 3d ed., p. 9, McGraw-Hill Book Company, Inc., New York, 1937.

reaction is taken to be at a pressure of 1 atm and without friction. Equation (6-15) then states that, when 1 mole of SO_2 and $\frac{1}{2}$ mole of O_2 react stoichiometrically (i.e., in accordance with the equation) at a temperature of 25°C and a pressure of 1 atm, the energy transferred from the system to the surroundings would be 23,450 cal. If Q or ΔH had a plus sign, the energy would have been transferred *to*, and not *from*, the system. This sign convention is usually, but not always, used.

Heat of Formation

The heat of formation of a substance is the value of ΔH for the reaction by which the substance is produced at given constant temperature and pressure from its elements. It is necessary to make clear the forms in which both the elements and the product exist during the reaction. For example, in the reaction of sulfur and oxygen to form sulfur dioxide, the reaction might be

$$S(\text{rhombic}) + O_2(g) \rightarrow SO_2(g) \qquad \Delta H_{25°C} = -70{,}940 \text{ cal} \qquad (6\text{-}16)$$

Correspondingly the reaction for formation of sulfur trioxide is

$$S(\text{rhombic}) + 1\tfrac{1}{2}O_2(g) \rightarrow SO_3(g) \qquad \Delta H_{25°C} = -94{,}390 \text{ cal} \tag{6-17}$$

Heats of formation of the elements in their stable forms at the temperature in question are taken as zero. For this reason, the heat of reaction ΔH in Eq. (6-16) is the heat of formation ΔH_f for $SO_2(g)$. Similarly, ΔH_f for $SO_3(g)$ is $-94{,}390$ cal/mole at 25°C from Eq. (6-17). Heats of formation are tabulated in the published literature for many of the substances encountered in engineering operations, and they are of great utility. A convenient tabulation of heats of formation will be found in Perry's "Handbook."[†]

Use of Heats of Formation

The heat of reaction, or enthalpy change for a reaction, can be determined by using tabulated values of heats of formation for the reactants and products of the reaction. The tabular data for heats of formation thus eliminate the need for specific informa-

[†] J. H. Perry (ed.), "Chemical Engineers' Handbook," 3d ed., McGraw-Hill Book Company, Inc., New York, 1950.

tion regarding every conceivable reaction. The heat of reaction at 1 atm and 25°C can be obtained by taking the difference between the sum of the heats of formation at 25°C for the products and that for the reactants. This procedure neglects the energy involved when the individual substances are mixed, but this is usually a small effect.

As a simple illustration of the use of heats of formation, let us subtract Eq. (6-16) from Eq. (6-17), which gives

$$\tfrac{1}{2}O_2(g) \rightarrow SO_3(g) - SO_2(g) \qquad \Delta H_{25°C} = -23,450 \text{ cal} \qquad (6-18)$$

When this equation is rearranged, it gives the information presented in Eq. (6-15). The values of heats of formation have thus been used to obtain the heat of a reaction. For additivity of thermochemical equations in this manner, the various reactions concerned must obviously be expressed for the same conditions of temperature and pressure.

Example 6-C. Carbon monoxide and oxygen in stoichiometric amounts are in a reaction vessel at 700°F and 1 atm. If the reaction

$$CO + \tfrac{1}{2}O_2 \rightleftharpoons CO_2$$

goes 5% toward stoichiometric completion at atmospheric pressure, what temperature (to the nearest 10°F) could theoretically be achieved?

Solution. The theoretical temperature is attained when all the enthalpy change for reaction appears as additional enthalpy of the product gases.

In Perry's "Handbook," 3d ed., p. 237, the enthalpies of formation ΔH_f at 25°C in kcal/mole for the three components are given as

CO	-26.416
O_2	0
CO_2	-94.052

The enthalpy change for the reaction given above is then

$$\Delta H = -94,052 - (-26,416) = -67,636 \text{ cal}$$

At 700°F or 371.1°C

$$\Delta H = -67,636 + \int_{298.2}^{644.3} (\Delta C_P) \, dT$$

The value of ΔC_P is obtained from the following values† for molal heat

† W. H. Walker, W. K. Lewis, W. H. McAdams, and E. R. Gilliland, "Principles of Chemical Engineering," 3d ed., p. 9, McGraw-Hill Book Company, Inc., New York, 1937.

capacities when T is temperature in degrees Kelvin:

$$C_{P,CO,O_2} = 6.76 + 0.000606T + 0.00000013T^2$$
$$C_{P,CO_2} = 7.70 + 0.0053T - 0.00000083T^2$$
$$\Delta C_P = -2.44 + 0.0044T - 0.0000010T^2$$

Then

$$\Delta H_{371.1°C} = -67{,}636 + \left[(-2.44)(644.3 - 298.2) \right.$$
$$\left. + \frac{0.0044}{2}(644.3^2 - 298.2^2) - \frac{0.0000010}{3}(644.3^3 - 298.2^3) \right]$$
$$= -67{,}636 - 844.5 + 717.6 - 80.3$$
$$= -67{,}843 \text{ cal}$$

If the reaction goes 5% to completion, the enthalpy change will be -3392 cal. This amount of energy will be required to raise 0.95 mole of CO, 0.475 mole of O_2, and 0.05 mole of CO_2 to $T°$K.

Therefore

$$3392 = \int_{644.3}^{T} (10.02 + 0.00113T + 0.000000143T^2)\,dT$$
$$= 10.02T + 0.000565T^2 + 0.000000048T^3$$
$$\qquad\qquad\qquad\qquad - 6456 - 234.5 - 12.84$$
$$10{,}097 = 10.02T + 0.000565T^2 + 0.000000048T^3$$

The value of T may be obtained by trial so that the right-hand side of the last equality equals 10,097.

Estimated T, $°K$	$\Delta = 10{,}097 - 10.02T - 0.000565T^2 - 0.000000048T^3$
1000	-505
960	-75
950	15

Therefore T may be taken as 950°K or 1250°F.

Determination of Heat of Formation

Heats of formation are usually determined by indirect methods from measurements of heats such as those of combustion, reaction, solution, fusion, and vaporization. If information is available, for example, on the heats of formation of all but a single participant in a reaction, the heat of formation of that compound can be developed from the heats of formation of the other substances and the measured heat of the reaction in question.

Heat determinations, such as those mentioned above, are usually made by calorimetric measurements most often carried out under conditions of constant volume. When the volume remains constant, W is zero, and it can be seen from Eq. (6-2) that the energy Q transferred through the walls of the calorimeter from the surroundings is equal to ΔE for the process occurring in the calorimeter.

Inasmuch as hydrocarbon compounds are of great interest to the chemical engineer, they afford an opportunity for discussing one of the main approaches to the procurement of heats of formation—namely, through calorimetric studies of heats of combustion. The reaction for combustion of a liquid hydrocarbon can be written in general form as follows:

$$C_nH_m(l) + \left(n + \frac{m}{4}\right) O_2(g) \rightarrow nCO_2(g) + \frac{m}{2} H_2O(l)$$

$$\Delta H = I \text{ cal} \quad (6\text{-}19)$$

If accurate data are available for the heats of formation of CO_2 and H_2O, it is apparent that, if ΔH for the reaction is measured for a given reference temperature, the value of ΔH_f for the formation of $C_nH_m(l)$ at that temperature can be obtained according to the equation

$$\Delta H_{f,C_nH_m(l)} = n \, \Delta H_{f,CO_2(g)} + \frac{m}{2} \, \Delta H_{f,H_2O(l)} - I \quad (6\text{-}20)$$

It will be noted that $\Delta H_{f,O_2(g)}$ is omitted, the value of ΔH_f for elemental forms being taken as zero at a given reference temperature. The precision of data obtained in calorimetric measurements is a function of the conditions under which measurements are made. It is possible, nevertheless, in combustion studies to achieve data precise to within 0.1% of the most probable values.

Calorimetry

In the operation of a calorimeter it is ordinary practice to obtain the energy change by indirect means for the reaction being studied. The heat capacity of the constant-volume calorimeter shown diagrammatically in Fig. 6-1 is determined by burning a standard compound having an accurately known heat of combustion or by introducing electrically a measured amount of energy and observing in either case the rise in temperature of the calorimeter for the known energy input. The energy equivalent of the calorimeter per degree of temperature rise is then known. Combustion of the unknown sample will give a temperature rise that can be compared with the heat capacity of the calorimeter to establish the energy change.   Calibration of the calorimeter, and actual measurements, are handled in such a manner as to keep the temperature rise small, e.g., 1 to 2°F.   Thus both

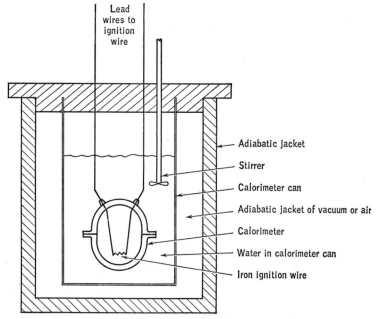

Fig. 6-1. Schematic diagram of combustion calorimeter.

measurements can be related closely to a specific temperature, usually taken as the mean value for the small observed temperature range.

A calorimeter can be operated with an adiabatic jacket to minimize thermal transfer to or from the surroundings.   The actual bomb is placed in a calorimeter can that has been filled with a weighed amount of water to increase the total heat capacity.   Outside the can there is an adiabatic jacket which may be an air gap or vacuum space, depending upon required precision.   Another type of adiabatic jacket would be provided by charging water into the gap and, by electrical means, keeping the water temperature at all times equal to the temperature of the can holding the bomb. In each instance there should be practically no energy transfer from the calorimeter can to the surroundings. The heat capacity of the calorimeter then is determined by the water in which the calorimeter is immersed, the bomb itself and its contents, and any miscellaneous leads to the calorimeter.

For solid compounds or liquids with low vapor pressures at room temperature, the energy change upon combustion is determined by use of a bomb having an initial pressure of oxygen of about 30 atm. An initial charge of water in the bomb of about 3 ml per liter of bomb volume is used so that the gas in the bomb is saturated with water at all times. The observed energy change is then for the case in which any water formed in the combustion process ends in the liquid state. In standardizing, it is the practice to use 3 g of pure benzoic acid per liter of bomb volume and initiate burning by passing an electric current through a fine iron wire in contact with the sample. A platinum wire could be used in place of the iron wire. In actual runs the sample size is determined as that amount required to give essentially the same temperature rise as did the selected amount of benzoic acid or other standard substance used in the calibration.

If the heat capacity of the calorimeter is known and the temperature rise is determined, the energy change resulting from the reaction can be calculated. It is necessary to make appropriate corrections for the electrical energy added, the burning of the iron wire, etc.

The quantity ΔE_{com} as observed experimentally for a given substance is not of value for purposes of tabulation since the operation of calorimeters probably will be under different conditions for different investigators. It is general practice to correct the result to the standard case of the energy change for the reaction when (1) the substance being studied is at its accepted standard state for the given temperature; (2) the oxygen is gaseous and at its standard state of 1 atm; and (3) the products, including CO_2 and H_2O are at their standard states of 1 atm with the CO_2 in the gas phase and the H_2O in the liquid phase. The value of ΔE_{st} is finally obtained from an equation of the form,

$$\Delta E_{st} = \Delta E_{com} + \Delta E_{cor} \qquad (6\text{-}21)$$

where ΔE_{st} = energy change for combustion of 1 mole of sample with reactants and products in their standard states

ΔE_{com} = observed energy change for 1 mole of sample in combustion at constant volume

ΔE_{cor} = correction term required to correct observed energy change for 1 mole of sample to the selected standard condition

The correction to give the standard state will ordinarily represent a few tenths of 1% of the measured value, but the high precision of modern calorimetry makes the correction worth considering. If the operation of the calorimeter is not at the standard temperature, the value of ΔE_{st} is obtained by correcting the value for a nearby temperature by use of the equation

$$d(\Delta E_{st}) = (\Delta C_V)\, dT \qquad (6\text{-}22)$$

For a solid or liquid reactant and the liquid H_2O formed, values of C_P are almost the same as values of C_V and so may be used in evaluation of ΔC_V, which is the difference between the heat capacities at constant volume for the products and for the reactants, each multiplied by the respective number of moles entering the reaction.

Finally, as indicated earlier, the value of ΔE_{st} does not find so much application as ΔH_{st}. From Eq. (6-3) the value of ΔH_{st} is

$$\Delta H_{st} = \Delta E_{st} + \Delta(PV)_{st} \qquad (6\text{-}23)$$

From the knowledge of ΔH_f for CO_2 and ΔH_f for water, the value of ΔH_{st} can be used to give ΔH_f at the desired standard state for the substance burned, in accordance with Eqs. (6-19) and (6-20).

Other types of calorimeters may be used and the same basic principles applied in the development of data for the heat of formation of a compound for a given standard state. Notable here would be the flame calorimeter for measuring heats of combustion of materials that are gaseous at room temperature and the heat-of-reaction calorimeter for measurements of energy changes in reactions such as the hydrogenation of hydrocarbons.

Example 6-D. A sample consisting of 0.2180 g of pure hexadecane is burned in a bomb calorimeter containing oxygen gas (18 atm before reaction) saturated with water vapor by having 3 g of liquid water present. The heat capacity of the bomb, its contents, and the surrounding jacket expressed as an equivalent weight of water is 1960 g. The corrected temperature rise is 1.254°C, and the calorimeter is operated essentially at 25°C. If the standard heat (enthalpy change) of formation of $CO_2(g)$ is $-94,052$ cal/mole and that for $H_2O(l)$ is $-68,317$ cal/mole at 25°C, what is the standard heat of formation of the hexadecane at that temperature?

Solution. The stoichiometric reaction is

$$C_{16}H_{34}(s) + 24\tfrac{1}{2}O_2(g) \rightarrow 16CO_2(g) + 17H_2O(l)$$

The difference between the volume of the hexadecane and liquid water in the bomb initially and the final volume of liquid water in the bomb may be neglected. The reaction in the gas phase is then at constant volume. The gases will be assumed to be perfect gases. In that case their internal energy is a function only of temperature. It may also be assumed that the energy of the nongaseous components is a function only of the temperature. Therefore the energy obtained from the system is not a pressure function.

$$\Delta E = Q_V = Q_P - \Delta(PV) = Q_P - \Delta n(\mathbf{R}T)$$

$$\Delta H_{\text{com}} = Q_P = Q_V + \Delta n\,(\mathbf{R}T) = -\frac{(1960)(1.254)(226.4)}{0.2180}$$

$$+ (-8.5)(1.987)(298.2)$$

$$\Delta H_{\text{com}} = -2,553,000 - 5040 = -2,558,000 \text{ cal/mole}$$

Then the standard enthalpy change for formation of hexadecane at 25°C is given by the equation

$$\Delta H_f = (16)(\Delta H_{f,\text{CO}_2}) + (17)(\Delta H_{f,\text{H}_2\text{O}}) - (24\tfrac{1}{2})(\Delta H_{f,\text{O}_2}) - \Delta H_{\text{com}}$$
$$\Delta H_f = (16)(-94,052) + (17)(-68,317) - 0 - (-2,558,000)$$
$$= -108,200 \text{ cal/mole} \quad \text{at } 25°C$$

Change of Heat of Reaction with Temperature

The enthalpy change for a reaction occurring at constant temperature with all of the reactants and products in their standard states (i.e., in their stable forms at the temperature in question and at an arbitrarily chosen standard-state pressure, usually 1 atm) is given the symbol $\Delta H°$. This quantity has a definite value for a given reaction at a given temperature, but the value is dependent on the arbitrary choice of the standard-state pressure.

In order to evaluate the change of $\Delta H°$ with change in temperature, it must be taken into account that the heat of reaction changes with temperature and that the enthalpy of each reactant and product changes with temperature. For any individual reactant or product, the latter change can be evaluated from the equation,

$$H^\circ_{T_2} - H^\circ_{T_1} = \int_{T_1}^{T_2} C^\circ_P \, dT \qquad (6\text{-}24)$$

in which C°_P is the heat capacity at a constant pressure of 1 atm for that substance. Because enthalpy is a state property, the enthalpy change between any two given states of a system will be the same, regardless of the particular steps or processes by which the change is carried out. If the enthalpy change between two given states of the system is evaluated for each of two different processes, they can then be equated. This fact furnishes a useful method of finding the variation of heat of reaction with change in temperature.

If the reactants, starting at 25°C, are raised in temperature without reacting until they are at temperature T and then allowed to react forming the products at temperature T, the change in enthalpy will be the same as though the reaction took place at 25°C with the products being then raised to temperature T. These changes can be indicated diagrammatically as follows, considering that 25°C is approximately equal to 298°K:

$$
\begin{array}{c}
\overset{\text{step 2}}{a\mathrm{A} + b\mathrm{B} \longrightarrow r\mathrm{R} + s\mathrm{S}} \qquad T = T^\circ\mathrm{K} \\[4pt]
{\scriptstyle\text{step 1}}\uparrow \qquad\quad \uparrow {\scriptstyle\text{step 4}} \\[4pt]
\underset{\text{step 3}}{a\mathrm{A} + b\mathrm{B} \longrightarrow r\mathrm{R} + s\mathrm{S}} \qquad T = 298^\circ\mathrm{K}
\end{array}
\qquad (6\text{-}25)
$$

Indicating the steps involved by subscripts, it follows that

$$\Delta H^\circ_1 + \Delta H^\circ_2 = \Delta H^\circ_3 + \Delta H^\circ_4 \qquad (6\text{-}26)$$

The values of ΔH°_1 and ΔH°_4 can be obtained by application of Eq. (6-24), and ΔH°_2 and ΔH°_3 are, respectively, the heats of reaction at $T^\circ\mathrm{K}$ and 298°K when all substances are in their standard states at the temperatures in question. Appropriate substitution in Eq. (6-26) gives

$$\Delta H^\circ_2 = \Delta H^\circ_T = \Delta H^\circ_{298^\circ\mathrm{K}}$$
$$+ \int_{298}^{T} [r(C^\circ_P)_\mathrm{R} + s(C^\circ_P)_\mathrm{S} - a(C^\circ_P)_\mathrm{A} - b(C^\circ_P)_\mathrm{B}] \, dT \qquad (6\text{-}27)$$

or

$$\Delta H^\circ_T = \Delta H^\circ_{298^\circ\mathrm{K}} + \int_{298}^{T} \Delta C^\circ_P \, dT \qquad (6\text{-}28)$$

With a knowledge of the heat capacities of reactants and products as functions of temperature, the standard heat of reaction at

25°C will serve to give the standard heat of reaction at any other temperature.

Example 6-E. From the following data† compute the enthalpy change of formation of NH_3 at 900°F:

$$\Delta H_{f,\text{NH}_3} \text{ at } 25°C = -10.96 \text{ kcal/mole}$$
$$C_{P,\text{NH}_3} = 6.70 + 0.0063T$$
$$C_{P,\text{N}_2} = 6.76 + 0.0006606T + 0.00000013T^2$$
$$C_{P,\text{H}_2} = 6.85 + 0.00028T + 0.00000022T^2$$

when T is in degrees Kelvin.

Solution. The reaction of interest is

$$\tfrac{1}{2}\text{N}_2(g) + \tfrac{3}{2}\text{H}_2(g) \rightarrow \text{NH}_3(g)$$

The enthalpy change of formation for the elements is taken as zero at 25°C and 1 atm. Therefore the enthalpy change for the above reaction is equal to the enthalpy change of formation of NH_3. The temperature of 900°F is equal to 518°C. The appropriate equation to give the enthalpy change of formation of NH_3 at 518°C or 791.2°K is

$$\Delta H_{f,\text{NH}_{3_{791.2}}} = \Delta H_{f,\text{NH}_{3_{298.2}}} + \int_{298.2}^{791.2} (\Delta C_P)\, dT$$
$$\Delta C_P = C_{P,\text{NH}_3} - \tfrac{1}{2}C_{P,\text{N}_2} - \tfrac{3}{2}C_{P,\text{H}_2}$$
$$= -6.96 + 0.0056T - 0.00000040T^2$$
$$\Delta H_{f,\text{NH}_{3_{791.2}}} = -10,960 - (6.96)(791.2 - 298.2)$$
$$+ (0.0028)(791.2^2 - 298.2^2) - (0.00000013)(791.2^3 - 298.2^3)$$
$$= -10,960 - 3433 + 1504 - 64$$
$$= -12,953 = -12,950 \text{ cal/mole}$$

† J. H. Perry (ed.), "Chemical Engineers' Handbook," 3d ed., p. 241, McGraw-Hill Book Company, Inc., New York, 1950.

W. H. Walker, W. K. Lewis, W. H. McAdams, and E. R. Gilliland, "Principles of Chemical Engineering," 3d ed., p. 9, McGraw-Hill Book Company, Inc., New York, 1937.

7

Energy Balances

An energy balance, like the material balance discussed in Chap. 5, is an accounting procedure which depends on the conservation principle. The balance, as in the earlier discussion, takes the form,

$$\text{Input} - \text{output} = \text{accumulation}$$

Such a balance can be used for any quantity that is conserved, such as matter, energy, or momentum.† Balances featuring energy are very useful in chemical engineering calculations because energy is both a necessary commodity in a large number of processes and one that costs enough to focus attention on economy in its use.

Constant-weight Systems

An energy balance for a system of constant weight (closed system) is expressed in Eq. (6-2), which states that $\Delta E = Q - W$. The quantities Q and W both represent energy inputs and outputs, depending upon sign, whereas ΔE represents accumulation.

Example 7-A. A sample consisting of 0.1 lb of a gas is confined in the space A of Fig. 7-A1 in a cylinder fitted with a piston C. The cylinder is immersed in an air bath B. The cylinder walls are thermally conducting, but the walls indicated by crosshatching in the figure are thermally insulated. The bath B contains 0.05 lb of air. It will be

† Momentum balances will not be treated in this book, but they are very useful in connection with fluid mechanics.

assumed that neither the piston nor the rod allows leakage of gas past it but nevertheless can be moved without friction.

At the start of the process the temperatures in spaces A and B have become equal and uniform. By applying a mean force of 520 lb to rod D, the piston is moved slowly downward a distance of 9 in. At the end of the process when the temperatures have become uniform again it is found that the temperature in the air bath has risen 15.6°F. It is desired to find the change in internal energy of the entire sample in A, and the change per pound of sample. The mean heat capacity of air for this purpose will be taken as 0.24 Btu/(lb)(°F).

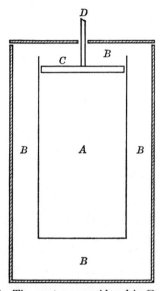

FIG. 7-A1. The system considered in Example 7-A.

Solution. In this case the air bath constitutes the surroundings in relation to thermal transfer.

$$W = -(520)(\tfrac{9}{12}) = -390 \text{ ft-lb} \qquad \text{or} \qquad \frac{-390}{778.2} = -0.501 \text{ Btu}$$

Because the energy transferred thermally to the system is equal in magnitude and opposite in sign to that transferred to the surroundings,

$$Q = -(0.05)(0.24)(15.6) = -0.187 \text{ Btu}$$

Then $\qquad \Delta E = -0.187 - (-0.501) = +0.314 \text{ Btu}$

or $\qquad 0.314/0.1 = 3.14 \text{ Btu/lb}$

Work in this process is negative because energy is being transferred mechanically *from* the surroundings. Heat is negative because energy is transferred thermally *to* the surroundings, causing the observed rise in their temperature. Because ΔE and Q are most frequently expressed in terms of Btu rather than in foot-pounds, W is most conveniently expressed in the same units.

Steady-flow System

A steady-flow system is different from a constant-weight system in two major regards. Material enters and leaves the system which thus becomes an open system. Material moves from place to place during the process and, although at any one point in the system the state of the material remains constant with respect to time, the state will vary from one point in the system to another further along the flow channel. These factors make necessary a somewhat different approach to an energy balance.

Because different parts of a flow system can be at different elevations, the potential energy of the fluid takes on importance which it did not have for a small constant-weight system with uniform properties throughout. Movement of the fluid through the flow channel involves kinetic energy, and this will vary from point to point if the velocity changes.

It is convenient to talk of different "forms" of energy, such as potential energy, kinetic energy, internal energy, surface energy (when energy is used to overcome surface tension effects), and electrical energy. This does not mean that the energy itself is different in these various instances, but that it is made manifest in different ways. It is thus possible for energy of one form to operate a process which results in energy appearing in another form. For example, electrical energy from a battery can be made, through the kinetic energy of a motor, to lift a weight and thus produce an increase in the potential energy of the weight, at the expense of the energy in its original form. Throughout all its changes in form, experiment verifies the fact that energy is conserved.

In a flow system, changes in the form of energy possessed by the fluid occur almost continuously, exchanges occurring among potential, kinetic, and internal energy as flow proceeds. For this reason, the analysis of flow processes must normally be extended to include all three of these forms.

In order to simplify matters, the present discussion will be limited to examples in which differences in potential and kinetic energy values between entrance and outlet sections of the flow stream are small enough to be neglected in comparison to other energy quantities involved. For many operations in industrial practice, the approximation thus involved is not serious. For example, suppose the outlet section is 10 ft above the inlet section. The change in potential energy of 1 lb of fluid would be 10 ft-lb/ lb, which when converted to Btu is $10/778.2 = 0.013$ Btu/lb.

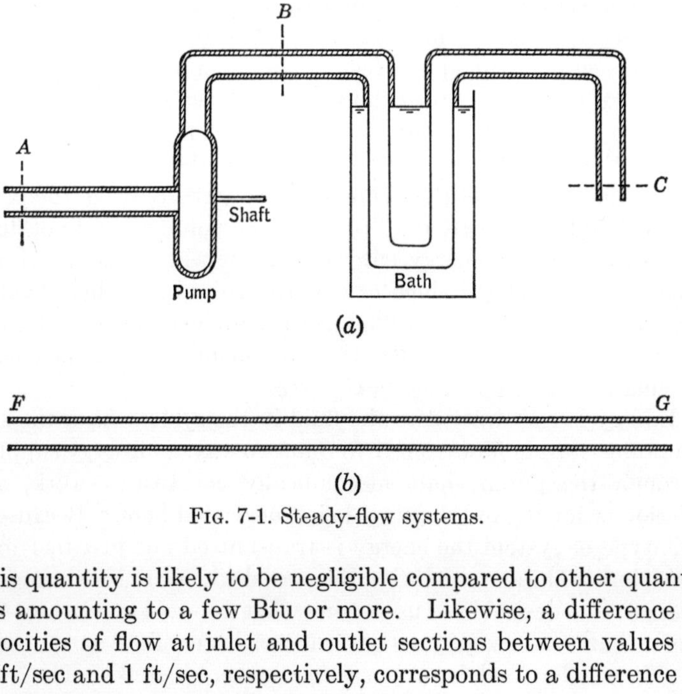

FIG. 7-1. Steady-flow systems.

This quantity is likely to be negligible compared to other quantities amounting to a few Btu or more. Likewise, a difference in velocities of flow at inlet and outlet sections between values of 10 ft/sec and 1 ft/sec, respectively, corresponds to a difference in kinetic energy of 0.002 Btu/lb.

Consider the steady-flow system shown diagrammatically in Fig. 7-1a, taking A as the entrance section and C as the outlet section. The crosshatched covering around parts of the flow channel represents thermal insulation. The pump is operated by energy supplied mechanically through the shaft. The fluid after leaving the pump passes through a portion of the channel which is submerged in a cooling bath. An energy balance for this system states that the energy entering the system at section

A plus any energy transmitted to the fluid from the surroundings during flow from A to C will equal the energy leaving the system at section C. Because the flow process is steady, there will be no accumulation term appearing in the balance.

Taking as a basis the time during which a unit weight of material enters at A, and neglecting potential and kinetic energy as discussed above, the energy that is characteristic of the 1 lb of material will be its internal energy E. There will also be energy required to push the pound of material into the system past the section A against the pressure existing there. This work energy corresponds to the action of a force through a distance. The force necessary is equal to the pressure at A in psf multiplied by the area of section A in square feet. The distance involved is that necessary to move 1 lb of fluid past the section, which will be equal to the volume in cubic feet of 1 lb of fluid divided by the area of the section A in square feet. When the force is multiplied by the distance to get the value of the energy involved, the product will be the pressure multiplied by the volume of 1 lb of fluid, or PV. Thus the energy entering the system at section A will equal $(E_A + P_A V_A)$, which can be recognized as being equal to H_A, the enthalpy of 1 lb of fluid at the state existing at section A. Similar reasoning shows that the corresponding value of energy leaving the system at section C is H_C.

Energy is transmitted to the fluid in the system from the surroundings during flow from A to C in two ways. Energy supplied through the pump shaft mechanically constitutes work, any friction occurring in the pump being neglected here. Because in this type of system the energy is transmitted not just to 1 lb of fluid, but to the system during the period when 1 lb is entering the system, it is desirable to use a somewhat different symbol for this work than was used in a constant-weight nonflow system, and so W' will be used for *flow systems* rather than W. The same convention in regard to sign will be used for both W and W', and in this case, because energy goes *to* the system mechanically, W' will be negative.

The second way in which energy is transferred between the system and the surroundings during flow from A to C is by thermal means in the cooling bath. This energy constitutes *heat* and is given the symbol Q' for the same reasons as before. In this case energy is transferred thermally to the surroundings, and Q' will be negative.

The energy balance can now be written† in equation form as

$$H_A + Q' - W' = H_c \qquad (7\text{-}1)$$

This equation may be rewritten as follows:

$$H_c - H_A = \Delta H = Q' - W' \qquad (7\text{-}2)$$

Equation (7-2) is applicable to all processes meeting the limitations outlined above. Although different from the energy balance equation, $\Delta E = Q - W$, for a constant-weight system, it can be seen to be very similar in form. Although the discussion of the steady-flow balance was based on the time during which 1 lb of fluid entered the system, there is no reason why 1 mole or any number of pounds or moles should not be used as the basis for calculation, provided that the values represented by all the symbols are changed correspondingly.

For the very simple system shown in Fig. 7-1b, suppose that a gaseous mixture consisting of 1 mole of SO_2 and $\frac{1}{2}$ mole of O_2 enters at section F, and, while flowing toward section G, the mixture reacts stoichiometrically to form SO_3. As shown in the figure, there is no device such as a pump whereby energy can be transferred, between F and G, to or from the surroundings mechanically. The crosshatched covering of the channel represents thermal insulation, and so thermal transfer is precluded. Because there can be neither Q' nor W' for this system, Eq. (7-2) shows that $\Delta H = O$, or that the enthalpy of 1 mole of SO_3 under the conditions existing at G will be equal to the enthalpy of 1 mole of SO_2 plus $\frac{1}{2}$ mole of O_2 under the conditions existing at F. The states of the system at the two sections will be very different; nevertheless, the enthalpy values will be equal. Because the channel shown is a simple one with no obstructions, and because changes in elevation and velocity are not significant, it would be expected that there would be little, if any, change in pressure during flow. The process can be described as an isobaric adiabatic steady-flow process, the term *adiabatic* signifying that there is no thermal transfer to or from the surroundings.

---

† This analysis neglects the energy changes resulting from viscous effects at the entrance and exit sections of the flow element. Also for a multi-component system it neglects transport of energy by diffusion. In both cases the energy effects are small relative to the changes ordinarily occurring in chemical process equipment. Details of the viscosity and diffusional effects will be encountered in more advanced studies of fluid flow.

If the insulation were to be removed from the steady-flow system of Fig. 7-1b but the reaction occurred during flow from F to G, a different energy balance result would be found. Equation (6-15) for this reaction shows that, when it takes place at constant temperature and pressure, ΔH is negative, which means that energy is transferred thermally from the system to the surroundings. It follows that, if during reaction as flow occurs from F to G, energy is transmitted thermally from the fluid to the surroundings rapidly enough to keep the temperature of the fluid constant, there will be an enthalpy decrease in the fluid of 23,450 cal/mole of SO_2 reacting.

The energy balance for this system, because W' is zero, becomes

$$\Delta H = Q' = -23,450 \text{ cal/mole } SO_2 \text{ entering} \qquad (7\text{-}3)$$

The product of reaction leaves section G at the same temperature as that found at F. In the adiabatic case discussed above, this thermal transfer of energy to the surroundings was not possible, and, as a result, the final temperature at section G would be much higher than that at entrance section F.

It can be seen by comparison of the two steady-flow processes related to Fig. 7-1b that, although the same energy balance equation is applicable, the values of the different quantities in it depend on the way the process is carried out. Each situation of this type which is met must be analyzed in terms of the conditions imposed upon the process.

Example 7-B. An equimolal mixture of H_2 and Cl_2 passes through an isobaric steady-flow reactor tube. The gas enters the reactor at a temperature of 500°F, and the reaction to form HCl gas is only partially complete when the gas leaves the reactor. At the outlet section, analysis of the gas shows a composition (by volume) of 10% H_2, 10% Cl_2, and 80% HCl, and its temperature is 800°F. What amount of heat is transferred to the reactor from the surroundings during this process?

Solution. From the given description of the process there is no indication that a pump or similar device for adding or removing energy mechanically is present. For this reason it will be assumed that W' is equal to zero. The energy balance statement in Eq. (7-2) then simplifies to $\Delta H = Q'$. Because Q' is the quantity sought, the problem becomes one of determining ΔH for the process.

Information regarding the reaction which is taking place in this reactor can be found in reference books. For example, Perry's "Handbook"† gives data to show that for the reaction

$$H_2(g) + Cl_2(g) \rightarrow 2HCl(g) \qquad \Delta H_{70°F} = -79,430 \text{ Btu/mole of } H_2$$

For the present calculation, the heat capacities (for constant pressure) of the substances involved will be taken equal to average values for the temperature ranges involved and treated as though constant. The following values in Btu/(mole)(°F) will be used: H_2, 7.00; Cl_2, 8.66; HCl, 7.29.

As was brought out in Chap. 6, the enthalpy of a system is a property which depends on the state of the system, and the change in enthalpy between a given initial state and a given final state will be the same, no matter how the process between the two states is carried out. This means that any convenient process can be chosen for consideration. In this case, one possibility is to cool the reactants from 500 to 70°F, allow the reaction to occur at that temperature to the extent indicated by the final gas analysis, and then raise the temperature of the products to 800°F. This procedure will take the system from its original state to its final state and will make use of the information regarding the change in enthalpy for the reaction occurring at constant pressure and a temperature of 70°F. In accordance with Eq. (6-6) for constant-pressure changes, the enthalpy changes for the cooling and heating steps of the proposed process can be determined by evaluating the heat quantities by means of the heat capacities and temperature changes involved.

For the first, or cooling step, choosing a basis of 1 mole of H_2 entering the system,

$$(\Delta H)_1 = [(1)(7.0) + (1)(8.66)](70 - 500)$$
$$= (15.66)(-430) = -6734 \text{ Btu}$$

For the reaction at 70°F, only 80% of the H_2 having reacted (0.8 mole),

$$(\Delta H)_2 = (0.80)(-79,430) = -63,544 \text{ Btu}$$

For the third, or heating, step, because the number of moles of gas is not changed by the reaction

$$(\Delta H)_3 = [(0.2)(7.0) + (0.2)(8.66) + (1.6)(7.29)](800 - 70)$$
$$= (14.79)(+730) = +10,797 \text{ Btu}$$

For the whole process,

$$\Delta H = -6734 - 63,544 + 10,797 = -59,481 = -59,500 \text{ Btu} = Q'$$

Instead of heat passing to the reactor, 59,500 Btu must be removed from the reactor for each mole of H_2 entering it.

† J. H. Perry (ed.), "Chemical Engineers' Handbook," 3d ed., McGraw-Hill Book Company, Inc., New York, 1950.

Example 7-C. What would be the temperature at the outlet section of the system of Example 7-B if the inlet conditions and the extent of reaction were to be the same as before, but the reactor walls were completely insulated? Assume for this purpose that the same heat capacity values can be used, and no dissociation occurs.

Solution. In this case both W' and Q' are equal to zero, and $\Delta H = 0$. Follow the same process as before except that the outlet temperature, instead of being 800°F will be t°F such that ΔH for the entire process equals zero.

$$\Delta H = -6734 - 63,544 + (14.80)(t - 70) = -71,314 + 14.80t = 0$$

$$t = \frac{71,314}{14.8} = 4820°F$$

This value is likely to be in some error because of probable changes in average heat capacity values over this wider range of temperature.

Example 7-D. Hydrogen gas enters a steady-flow system at 700°F and 500 psia at the rate of 1000 ft³/hr when measured under those conditions. Through another pipe, nitrogen gas at 900°F enters the system at a pressure of 40 psia and a rate of 4400 ft³/hr. The nitrogen passes through a steady-flow compressor, leaving it at 500 psia. The two gas streams mix, partial reaction occurs, and the products leave the system at 500 psia and an unknown temperature. If the compressor requires energy mechanically at the rate of 80,000 Btu/hr and thermal losses through the walls of the system amount to 10,000 Btu/hr, what is the change in enthalpy between entrance and outlet sections during admission of each 1000 ft³ of hydrogen when measured at 70°F and 1 atm absolute pressure?

Solution. For this steady-flow system, $\Delta H = Q' - W'$. On a preliminary basis of 1 hr of operation, $\Delta H = -10,000 - (-80,000) = +70,000$ Btu/hr.

Assuming that hydrogen behaves as a perfect gas, the rate of entry of H_2 when measured at 70°F and 1 atm is $(1000)(500/14.7)(460 + 70)/(460 + 700) = 15,540$ ft³/hr.

From these figures, the enthalpy change occurring for each entering 1000 ft³ of hydrogen (measured at 70°F and 1 atm) = $(70,000)(1000/15,540) = 4500$ Btu.

8

Introduction to Chemical Equilibria

The Equilibrium Constant

An introduction to chemical equilibria can best be based on the ideas of the dynamic situation existent among molecules in a vessel. For example, consider the very simple case in which only R and S molecules are present and are related in accordance with the chemical reaction, restricted to constant temperature and pressure,

$$R \rightleftharpoons S \tag{8-1}$$

At any given time, molecules of R are transforming into molecules of S and vice versa. The rate of transformation of R into S at a specific instant can be expressed mathematically for the simplest case as

$$- \frac{d(R)}{d\theta} = k[R] \tag{8-2}$$

Here the parentheses are used to designate the concentration of R, and the brackets represent the effective concentration.†

---

† See E. H. Swift, "Introductory Quantitative Analysis," p. 81, Prentice-Hall, Inc., Englewood Cliffs, N. J., 1950.

The *effective concentration* is an expression of the actual effect of the concentration of a particular species involved in a chemical reaction. It is related to the concentration by an equation of the form

$$\text{Effective concentration} = (\gamma)(\text{concentration})$$

The effective concentration is also called the *activity* and is a dimensionless quantity. The term γ is then the ratio of the effective concentration to the

Example 8-A. The compressibility factor Z is the ratio of the pressure-volume product PV for a real gas to that for a perfect gas for the same temperature and pressure. The pressure-volume product for a perfect gas is equal to $\mathbf{n}RT$. Therefore $Z = PV/\mathbf{n}RT$. For a gaseous pure substance, show the relationship between the activity coefficient when the gas-phase activity is based on pressure and the activity coefficient for the case in which concentration is used as a basis. Compare the units of the two activity coefficients.

Solution. Assume in each case that the standard state is the pure gas in the perfect-gas state at a pressure of 1 atm. Therefore the activities computed for each basis will be equal. For the activity based upon pressure,

$$a = \gamma_P P \tag{8-A1}$$

If the pressure is expressed in psi, then the units for γ_P are psi^{-1}. With concentration as the basis of computation

$$a = \gamma_c C \tag{8-A2}$$

If C is expressed in terms of moles/ft^3, then the units of γ_c are ft^3/mole. Now Eqs. (8-A1) and (8-A2) can be combined to give

$$\gamma_P = \gamma_c \frac{C}{P}$$

The quantity C for a pure substance is the number of moles per unit volume, $\mathbf{n}/V$, so that

$$\gamma_P = \frac{\gamma_c \mathbf{n}}{PV}$$

Numerator and denominator may be multiplied by $\mathbf{R}T$ and the definition of Z used to give

$$\gamma_P = \frac{\gamma_c \mathbf{n} \mathbf{R} T}{\mathbf{R} T P V} = \frac{\gamma_c}{Z \mathbf{R} T}$$

---

actual concentration and is called an *activity coefficient*, having the inverse dimensions of concentration. In many instances it is more convenient to use mole fraction or partial pressure in place of concentration. In these cases the magnitude and dimensions of the corresponding activity coefficients would be different from that used in the equation above.

For very dilute solutions or gas mixtures at very low pressures the numerical value of the activity coefficient approaches unity. In many instances, for lack of specific data on activity coefficients, it becomes necessary to assume such ideal behavior as a working approximation. In calculations in this book the activity coefficients will be taken as unity. Later work in physical chemistry will allow the student to see how activity coefficients may be treated for the nonideal conditions.

If the gas is perfect, Z has the value of 1, and in engineering units γ_P is 1 psi^{-1}. Then γ_C is equal to $\mathbf{R}T$ ft^3/mole when $\mathbf{R}$ and T are expressed in consistent units.

Equation (8-2) states that the rate of decrease of concentration of R with respect to time is equal to a constant k multiplied by the activity of R. The constant k is called the *specific reaction-rate constant*, and it is a function of the temperature of the system. Likewise for component S and its transformation into R, there is the expression

$$-\frac{d(\mathrm{S})}{d\theta} = k'[\mathrm{S}] \qquad (8\text{-}3)$$

in which k' is the specific reaction-rate constant for the reaction involving the disappearance of S. Inasmuch as the disappearance of S results in the formation of R according to Eq. (8-1), a combination of Eqs. (8-2) and (8-3) can be made to give the *net* rate of disappearance of R as

$$-\left[\frac{d(\mathrm{R})}{d\theta}\right]_{\mathrm{net}} = k[\mathrm{R}] - k'[\mathrm{S}] \qquad (8\text{-}4)$$

A point is finally reached at which the net change in R is zero; that is, the rate of disappearance of R to give S is just equal to the rate of formation of R from S. Figure 8-1 shows the concentration of R as a function of time, and that there is an asymptotic approach to the value $(\mathrm{R})_{\theta=\infty}$. In the actual situation an infinite time would not be required because of minor fluctuations in temperature in the real case. When no further net change

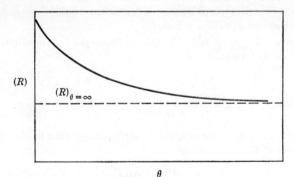

FIG. 8-1. Concentration versus time for a simple first-order reversible reaction.

occurs in the system, and it has reached a state of equilibrium, $d(R)/d\theta$ becomes zero, and Eq. (8-4) gives

$$k[R] = k'[S] \tag{8-5}$$

This equation may then be used to define the state of chemical equilibrium.

If we define an equilibrium constant at constant temperature as

$$K = \frac{k}{k'} \tag{8-6}$$

then Eq. (8-5) becomes

$$K = \frac{[S]}{[R]} \tag{8-7}$$

It is seen then that the equilibrium constant is the ratio of the activities of the product and the reactant at equilibrium. The general reaction

$$lL + mM + nN \cdots \rightleftharpoons rR + sS + tT \cdots \tag{8-8}$$

would have an equilibrium constant defined as

$$K = \frac{[R]^r[S]^s[T]^t \cdots}{[L]^l[M]^m[N]^n \cdots} \tag{8-9}$$

Example 8-B. The homogeneous reaction for the dehydrogenation of ethane can be written as follows:

$$C_2H_6 \rightleftharpoons C_2H_4 + H_2$$

The reaction-rate constant for the forward reaction at 551°C is 2.8×10^{-5} sec^{-1}, and the constant for the reverse reaction at that temperature is 7.76×10^{-2} liter/(mole)(sec). What is the equilibrium constant at 551°C expressed in pressure units?

Solution. At equilibrium the rate of decomposition of ethane equals the rate of its formation, or

$$k_C(C_{C_2H_6}) = k_C'(C_{C_2H_4})(C_{H_2})$$

Then
$$\frac{k_C}{k_C'} = \frac{(C_{C_2H_4})(C_{H_2})}{(C_{C_2H_6})} = K_C \tag{8-B1}$$

If perfect gases are assumed, the latter equation may be converted to K_P by use of the relationship

$$PV = nRT$$

or
$$C = \frac{P}{RT} \tag{8-B2}$$

Substitution of Eq. (8-B2) in Eq. (8-B1) gives

$$\frac{k_C}{k_C'} = \frac{(p_{C_2H_4})(p_{H_2})}{RT(p_{C_2H_6})} = \frac{K_P}{RT}$$

or
$$K_P = \left(\frac{k_C}{k_C'}\right) RT$$

$$= \left(\frac{2.8 \times 10^{-5}}{7.76 \times 10^{-2}}\right)(0.08206)(824.2) \text{ atm}$$

$$= 2.44 \times 10^{-2} \text{ atm}$$

The true thermodynamic equilibrium constant K at 551°C is 6.3×10^{-2} with each gas at a standard state of unit pressure and behaving as a perfect gas. This constant has no units. If the assumption is made that each activity coefficient is unity, the value of K_P based on K is 6.3×10^{-2} atm. The difference between this value and the one computed from the rate constants results from the assumption of unit activities and from differences in experimental data.

With a knowledge of K, the molecular species present in a reacting system (a priori knowledge), and a material balance involving each of the kinds of atoms in the system, means exist for describing the theoretical yields in a reacting mixture. Fortunately, data are available for the computation of K for many combinations of molecules. Unfortunately there are blanks in the systematized tabulation of the appropriate thermodynamic data, and one cannot help but be chagrined occasionally at the lack of information for solving the particular problem at hand. Here, in reality, lies one of the great challenges to the chemical engineer—the challenge of developing data by extrapolation, statistical and quantum mechanics, judicious guessing, etc.

The equilibrium constant K can be evaluated by use of a quantity called the free-energy change at standard state.† It is designated as $\Delta F°$, where the degree sign designates the standard state. The relation between the standard free-energy change and the equilibrium constant K is given as

$$-\Delta F° = RT \ln K \qquad (8\text{-}10)$$

Tabulations of $F°$ for many compounds are available.‡ By taking the algebraic sum of the standard free energies for a reaction

† This thermodynamic function receives detailed treatment in standard textbooks on physical chemistry.

‡ Ordinarily referred to the elements required to form the compound.

such as that given in Eq. (8-8) the value of $\Delta F°$ is developed as follows:

$$\Delta F° = (rF_R° + sF_S° + tF_T° + \cdots) - (lF_L° + mF_M° + nF_N° + \cdots)$$
$$(8\text{-}11)$$

The standard reference state is ordinarily a function only of temperature. If that is the case, it can be seen from Eq. (8-10) that the equilibrium constant is also a function of temperature only.

Standard States and Standard Free-energy Changes

Since the standard reference state is arbitrarily defined at a given temperature, it can conveniently be taken as the same state by each investigator who reports data. Agreement has been achieved, in the main, as to what states are standard, and so data taken from one source can usually be used with data from another source. As a word of caution, though, it should be understood clearly what standard states are in use in a given tabulation.

Tabulations of standard free-energy data are usually at 25°C. The standard state for a gas is most frequently taken as a perfect gas at the temperature of interest and at a pressure of 1 atm. For a solid, the standard state at a given temperature is the stable solid form at that temperature and a pressure of 1 atm. For a liquid, the state of the pure liquid at the temperature of interest and a pressure of 1 atm is used. When the temperature in question differs from 25°C for which tabulated values are usually found, it becomes necessary to convert the values to correspond to the other temperature.

Use of Standard Free-energy Data

Equation (8-10) states that all one need do to obtain a value for a thermodynamic equilibrium constant at the standard-state temperature is to obtain free-energy data from a tabulation of values for the pure components at the standard state, and develop the algebraic sum according to the stoichiometry of the reaction under consideration. The sum can be inserted in Eq. (8-10) and K computed at the given temperature. It is reasonably apparent that the numerical value of K will depend on the selected standard state. Even though the numerical value can vary according to the standard state used in a given set of data, the same final results for equilibrium concentrations in a specific chemical reaction would be obtained in sets of calculations based on other standard states.

As an example of the way in which Eq. (8-10) can be used as a tool, the reaction

$$H_2(g) + Cl_2(g) \rightleftharpoons 2HCl(g) \qquad (8\text{-}12)$$

can be analyzed to determine the equilibrium concentrations of H_2, Cl_2, and HCl at 25°C and 1 atm when 1 mole of H_2 and 1 mole of Cl_2 are initially present. From Table 197 in the third edition of Perry's "Handbook," values of $F°$ for various compounds in the standard state at 25°C relative to the elements *in their standard states* at 25°C are given. Such values are called the free energies of formation for the standard states. Actually these values are changes in free energy for the processes when the compounds are formed from their elements, and all substances are in their standard states. At 25°C, then

$$F°_{H_2} = 0$$
$$F°_{Cl_2} = 0$$
$$F°_{HCl} = -22.778 \text{ kcal/mole}$$

so that, for the reaction shown in Eq. (8-12) at 25°C and 1 atm,

$$-\Delta F° = 45{,}556 \text{ cal/mole} = \mathbf{R}T \ln K$$
$$\ln K = \frac{45{,}556}{1.987 \times 298} = 76.8$$
$$K = 2.24 \times 10^{33}$$

For a perfect gas, the activity may be taken as numerically equal to the partial pressure of the gas expressed in atmospheres when the standard state is the perfect gas at 1 atm. The *partial pressure* of any component may be defined as the product of the total pressure and the mole fraction of the component. From the stoichiometry of Eq. (8-12), letting x equal the fraction of the original moles of H_2 which remain at equilibrium, the mole fraction for each component is derived as follows:

Initial moles of H_2	$= 1$
Initial moles of Cl_2	$= 1$
Final moles of H_2	$= x$
Final moles of Cl_2	$= x$
Final moles of HCl	$= 2 - 2x$
Total final moles	$= 2$
Final mole fraction of H_2	$= x/2$
Final mole fraction of Cl_2	$= x/2$
Final mole fraction of HCl	$= 1 - x$

Substitution of partial pressures in the equilibrium expression for Eq. (8-12) for a pressure of 1 atm gives

$$K = \frac{[(1 - x)(1)]^2}{[(x/2)(1)][(x/2)(1)]} = 2.24 \times 10^{33}$$

$$x = 4.23 \times 10^{-17}$$

Thus at 25°C this reaction goes essentially to completion, and the residual amounts of H_2 and Cl_2 are negligible.

Change of Equilibrium Constant with Temperature

Both sides of Eq. (8-10) may be divided by T, and the resultant expression differentiated with respect to T at constant pressure to give

$$\left(\frac{\partial \ln K}{\partial T}\right)_P = \frac{1}{R}\left[\frac{\partial(-\Delta F°/T)}{\partial T}\right]_P \qquad (8\text{-}13)$$

Equation (8-13) is thus an expression showing the change in the equilibrium constant with temperature at constant pressure. It may be written in a more useful form by noting that thermodynamics can be utilized to give

$$\frac{1}{R}\left[\frac{\partial(-\Delta F°/T)}{\partial T}\right]_P = \frac{\Delta H°}{RT^2} \qquad (8\text{-}14)$$

A combination of Eq. (8-13) and (8-14) yields

$$\left(\frac{\partial \ln K}{\partial T}\right)_P = \frac{\Delta H°}{RT^2} \qquad (8\text{-}15)$$

If the use of $\Delta H°$ is restricted to changes for which pressure is constant, or to cases in which $\Delta H°$ is not affected by pressure, the left side of Eq. (8-15) can be treated as a total differential to give the following equation, which is named for van't Hoff and is of great value in computations on chemical equilibria:

$$\frac{d \ln K}{dT} = \frac{\Delta H°}{RT^2} \qquad (8\text{-}16)$$

In Eq. (8-15), $\Delta H°$ is the enthalpy change for the reaction of interest when the reactants and products are in the standard states used as a basis in the preparation of the free-energy data required in the computation of the equilibrium constant K. In order to integrate Eq. (8-15), it is necessary to evaluate $\Delta H°$ as a function of temperature for the pressure of interest. The integration gives K as a function of temperature at constant pressure. For convenience, standard states that are not pressure functions are usually selected. Therefore the values of K at the different temperatures are valid for all pressures at those temperatures.

The specific evaluation of $\Delta H°$ as a function of temperature was discussed in Chap. 6, and Eq. (6-28) shows the relationship. Substitution of this equation in Eq. (8-16) for integration at constant pressure or when $\Delta H°$ is not a pressure function gives

$$ RT^2 \left(\frac{d \ln K}{dT} \right) = \Delta H°_{298°K} + \int_{298°K}^{T} \Delta C°_P \, dT \qquad (8\text{-}17) $$

This equation is useful because it gives a convenient means for developing the equilibrium constant K as a function of temperature from enthalpy data at 25°C and a knowledge of heat capacities at constant pressure for the temperature range of interest.

Example 8-C. Compute the value of the equilibrium constant for the reaction

$$ CO + \tfrac{1}{2}O_2 \rightleftharpoons CO_2 $$

at a temperature of 1500°F using the following data:†

Component	Free energy of formation[a] at 25°C, kcal/mole	Enthalpy of formation[a] at 25°C, kcal/mole
CO	−32.808	−26.416
O₂	0	0
CO₂	−94.260	−94.052

[a] The standard state at 25°C is the perfect gas at a pressure of 1 atm.

Molal heat capacities‡ at constant pressure, in cal/(mole)(°K), with T expressed in degrees Kelvin:

For CO, O₂: $C_P = 6.76 + 0.000606T + 0.00000013T^2$
For CO₂: $C_P = 7.70 + 0.0053T - 0.00000083T^2$

† J. H. Perry (ed.), "Chemical Engineers' Handbook," 3d ed., McGraw-Hill Book Company, Inc., New York, 1950.
‡ W. H. Walker, W. K. Lewis, W. H. McAdams, and E. R. Gilliland, "Principles of Chemical Engineering," 3d ed., p. 9, McGraw-Hill Book Company, Inc., New York, 1937.

Solution. At 25°C the equilibrium constant may be computed as follows:

$$-\Delta F^\circ = -(-94{,}260 + 32{,}808) = \mathbf{R}T \ln K = (1.987)(298.2) \ln K$$
$$\ln K = \frac{61{,}452}{(1.987)(298.2)} = 103.8$$

The change in $\ln K$ as a function of T is obtained from

$$\frac{d \ln K}{dT} = \frac{\Delta H^\circ}{\mathbf{R}T^2}$$

Here ΔH° must be written as a temperature function, and that is done as follows:

$$\Delta H_T^\circ = \Delta H_{298.2}^\circ + \int_{298.2}^{T} (\Delta C_P)\, dT$$
$$\Delta H_{298.2}^\circ = -94{,}052 + 26{,}416 = -67{,}636$$
$$\Delta C_P = -2.44 + 0.0044T - 0.0000010T^2$$
$$\Delta H_T^\circ = -67{,}095 - 2.44T + 0.0022T^2 - 0.00000033T^3$$

Then

$$\ln K_T - 103.8 = \frac{1}{\mathbf{R}} \int_{298.2}^{1124.3} \left(\frac{-67{,}095}{T^2} - \frac{2.44}{T} \right.$$
$$\left. + 0.0022 - 0.00000033T \right) dT$$
$$= -81.95 - 1.78 + 0.91 - 0.10$$
$$\ln K_T = 20.88$$
$$K_T = 1.12 \times 10^9$$

Thus the equilibrium lies far to the right at 1500°F, and so CO with stoichiometric amounts of oxygen would be quantitatively oxidized to CO_2 under ordinary conditions of pressure.

9

Introduction to Chemical Kinetics

Chemical kinetics is a study of the rate at which chemical reactions occur. Reaction rates are important in the design of processes because they determine the size of equipment required to achieve specified yields and therefore have much to do with economic feasibility. When time is not a factor, thermodynamics can describe theoretical yields and energy requirements. Usually, however, in actual situations time is a factor, and so the chemical engineer must understand how to deal with the relationship between time and composition.

Rate Equations for Homogeneous Reactions

Reaction-rate equations could be written in terms of pressure, density, volume, etc., but, because of the prime concern with concentration, they are usually written to show the change of concentration with time. For the simplest case in which a compound is decomposing irreversibly in a homogeneous or single-phase reaction, the stoichiometry may be written as

$$A \rightarrow R + S + \cdots \tag{9-1}$$

The reaction-rate expression might have the form

$$-\frac{d(A)}{d\theta} = k[A] \tag{9-2}$$

This equation states that the rate of disappearance of component A is equal to the activity of A multiplied by a constant.

97

Experimental data would have to be collected to prove or disprove the applicability of Eq. (9-2) to the particular case. Practically speaking, the study of reaction kinetics is strictly empirical, and the only way to develop rate equations is by experiment. For example, if experimental work showed k in Eq. (9-2) to be constant for various conditions at a given temperature, then that equation would be considered as representing the kinetics of the reaction. Because the exponent of [A] is 1, the reaction is said to be "first order" with respect to the component A. In the general case, reactions are more complex than the simple first-order example that was selected.

The general rate statement for noncomplex homogeneous reactions of the type

$$lL + mM + nN + \cdots \rightleftharpoons rR + sS + tT + \cdots \quad (9\text{-}3)$$

when considering the rate of disappearance of component L would be

$$-\frac{d(L)}{d\theta} = k[L]^l[M]^m[N]^n \cdots - k'[R]^r[S]^s[T]^t \cdots \quad (9\text{-}4)$$

Because the activity of a component is dimensionless, Eqs. (9-2) and (9-4) indicate that the specific reaction-rate constants must have the units of concentration divided by time.

As mentioned, the form of a rate equation is determined experimentally, and often the activity is replaced by the concentration. The uncertainty between using activity or concentration as a potential is associated with the empirical state of chemical kinetics. If concentrations were found experimentally to give constant values for the rate constants, then one could express the rate equation in terms of concentrations. Likewise if activities gave better results, they could be used. From a fundamental point of view, activities would seem best for use in rate equations. Often, however, data on activities are not available, and one has no choice but to use concentrations. If concentrations are used, Eq. (9-4) takes the form

$$-\frac{d(L)}{d\theta} = k_C(L)^l(M)^m(N)^n \cdots - k_C'(R)^r(S)^s(T)^t \cdots \quad (9\text{-}5)$$

The units of k_C and k_C' would be such that, when each is multiplied by its associated concentration terms, the results would have the units of a concentration divided by time. Thus k_C has the units of

$$(\text{Time})^{-1} (\text{concentration})^{1-(l+m+n+\cdots)}$$

and k_C' the units of

$$(\text{Time})^{-1} (\text{concentration})^{1-(r+s+t+\cdots)}$$

Decomposition of NO

An example of the treatment of rate data can be developed using the homogeneous gas-phase reaction

$$2NO(g) \rightleftharpoons N_2(g) + O_2(g) \tag{9-6}$$

For a one-cubic-foot vessel initially filled with nitric oxide at an absolute pressure of 14.7 psi, it is desired to know the time required to decompose 30% of the nitric oxide at a temperature of 4500°R. The rate of decomposition of the nitric oxide may be expressed simply as

$$-\frac{d(\text{NO})}{d\theta} = k[\text{NO}]^2 - k'[\text{N}_2][\text{O}_2] \tag{9-7}$$

Hougen and Watson[†] give values of k and k' for 4500°R as

$$k = 0.893 \text{ mole}/(\text{ft}^3)(\text{min})$$
$$k' = 0.00298 \text{ mole}/(\text{ft}^3)(\text{min})$$

Under the conditions of the problem, perfect-gas behavior may be assumed. Therefore the activity of a component can be taken as numerically, but not dimensionally, equal to the partial pressure of the component when the standard state is the perfect gas at a pressure of 1 atm and the given temperature. If C_0 is the initial concentration of NO and x is the amount of NO converted, both expressed in lb/ft³ of system; N_{NO} is the mole fraction of NO; and π is the total pressure in atmospheres; then the activity of NO for a pressure of 1 atm becomes

$$[\text{NO}] = N_{\text{NO}}\pi = \frac{(C_0 - x)(1)}{C_0} = \frac{C_0 - x}{C_0} \tag{9-8}$$

[†] O. A. Hougen and K. M. Watson, "Chemical Process Principles," part III, "Kinetics and Catalysis," p. 815, John Wiley & Sons, Inc., New York, 1947.

Likewise the activities of N_2 and O_2 are obtained as follows:

$$[N_2] = [O_2] = N_{N_2}\pi = \frac{(x/2)(1)}{C_0} = \frac{x}{2C_0} \qquad (9\text{-}9)$$

The numerical value of C_0 can be calculated in the following manner:

$$C_0 = \frac{P}{RT} = \frac{14.7}{(10.732)(4500)} = 0.000304 \text{ mole/ft}^3 \qquad (9\text{-}10)$$

Substitution of the appropriate quantities in Eq. (9-7) gives

$$\frac{dx}{d\theta} = k \left[\frac{C_0 - x}{C_0} \right]^2 - k' \left[\frac{x}{2C_0} \right]^2 \qquad (9\text{-}11)$$

For the case in which 30% of the NO is to be decomposed, it can be seen that neglect of the last term of this equation is reasonable, because, when the conversion has reached the stipulated extent,

$$\frac{k \left(\dfrac{C_0 - x}{C_0} \right)^2}{k' \, (x/2C_0)^2} = \frac{0.893}{0.00298} \frac{(0.7)^2}{(0.15)^2} = 65.3 \times 10^2 \qquad (9\text{-}12)$$

The large value for the ratio indicates that the second term on the right-hand side of Eq. (9-11) is less than 0.02% of the first term when the second term has its largest value relative to the first term. Then, neglecting the small term,

$$\frac{C_0^2}{k} \int_0^{0.3C_0} \frac{dx}{(C_0 - x)^2} = \int_0^\theta d\theta \qquad (9\text{-}13)$$

$$0.43 \frac{C_0}{k} = \theta$$

or

$$\theta = \frac{(0.43)(0.000304)}{0.893} = 0.000146 \text{ min}$$

The decomposition of NO at 4500°R is shown to be very rapid.

Reactions in Flow Systems

The calculation made above shows an attack for analysis of nonflow reactors. Industrial operations also require the design of flow reactors. Such design generally is very complex, but a simplified approach is often applicable. This simplification has reference to a so-called "plug flow." In that flow there are no concentration, pressure, temperature, or velocity gradients except in a single coordinate direction, and there is steady flow. The coordinate direction is the one corresponding to the bulk flow of the system.

Consider a pipe that is being used as a reactor. Schematically it may be shown as in Fig. 9-1. Cylindrical coordinates may be used to describe any point in the reactor. If plug flow prevails, there are no gradients in the r or ϕ directions, only in the z direction. The element of volume dV_R, under the conditions described, may be likened to a plug on the end of string that is being pulled through the reactor. A material balance over that

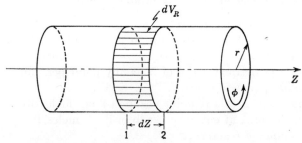

FIG. 9-1. Element of volume in a cyclindrical reactor.

element of volume gives the basic design equation for the reactor. Application of the general conservation relation

$$\text{Input} - \text{output} = \text{accumulation} \qquad (9\text{-}14)$$

gives for a steady state, for which there is no accumulation,

$$\text{Input} = \text{output} \qquad (9\text{-}15)$$

The only flow into the element is through the $r\phi$ plane in the z direction at section 1. Flow out is in the z direction through the $r\phi$ plane at section 2. The disappearance of the component of interest as a result of reaction may be looked upon as an exit stream. Another approach is offered by the revised equation

$$\text{Input} - \text{output} + \text{sources} - \text{sinks} = \text{accumulation} \qquad (9\text{-}16)$$

The significance of the terms will appear if the equation is applied, for example, to a component A for a differential period of time $d\theta$ during which conditions are taken as constant for the element of volume under consideration. The terms *input* and *output* represent the weights of component A entering and leaving the entrance and exit sections, respectively, during the time $d\theta$. They constitute exchanges between the element and the surroundings. The term *source* represents the weight of component A produced within the element in the time $d\theta$. The term *sink* represents the weight of component A which disappears within the element in that time. Sources and sinks are contributed, for example, by chemical reactions which either produce or use up component A as such. *Accumulation* is the increase in weight of component A in the element of time $d\theta$. For steady state, of course, it is zero.

The following nomenclature used by Hougen and Watson[†] will be convenient in the study of flow reactors:

F = total flow rate, lb/sec

x_A = moles of A converted up to any point per lb of fluid, moles/lb

r_A = rate of disappearance of A at any point per unit volume, moles/(sec)(ft^3)

n_A = moles of A at any point per lb of fluid, moles/lb

n_{A_0} = moles of A at entrance per lb of fluid, moles/lb

V_R = volume of reactor, ft^3

For a time $d\theta$, the material balance for component A for the element of volume dV_R is, in accordance with Eq. (9-16), when both accumulation and sources are equal to zero

$$F n_A - \left[F n_A + \frac{d(F n_A)}{dz} \, dz \right] - r_A \, dV_R = 0 \qquad (9\text{-}17)$$

or

$$- d(F n_A) = r_A \, dV_R \qquad (9\text{-}18)$$

At steady state F is a constant, and reference to the nomenclature shows that

$$n_A = n_{A_0} - x_A \qquad (9\text{-}19)$$

Therefore

$$d(F n_A) = F \, dn_A = -F \, dx_A \qquad (9\text{-}20)$$

Substitution of Eq. (9-20) in Eq. (9-18) gives

$$F \, dx_A = r_A \, dV_r \qquad (9\text{-}21)$$

[†] O. A. Hougen and K. M. Watson, "Chemical Process Principles," part III, "Kinetics and Catalysis," p. 832, John Wiley & Sons, Inc., New York, 1947.

Equation (9-21) is the design equation for a plug-flow reactor. It should be noted that, in addition to the restrictions already stated for plug flow, Eq. (9-17) and therefore Eq. (9-21) have the restriction that the only transport of A to section 1 and out of section 2 is by bulk flow; diffusion is neglected.

Example 9-A. A mixture of ozone and oxygen is passing through a tubular reactor at a pressure of 1 atm, a temperature of 212°F, and a velocity of 0.05 ft/sec. Plug flow prevails, and it is steady state. If the entering mixture is 10% ozone, what length of tube is required to decompose 50% of the ozone? The reaction may be written as

$$2O_3 \rightarrow 3O_2$$

and the specific reaction-rate constant in the equation

$$\text{Rate} = k_c(O_3)^2$$

is $(8.6 \times 10^{-2})(\text{liter})/(\text{g mole})(\text{sec})$

Solution. For convenience, a unit cross section may be used in the calculations. Perfect gases are assumed. The specific reaction-rate constant in engineering units is

$$k_c = (8.6 \times 10^{-2})(16.019) = 1.378 \text{ ft}^3/(\text{lb mole})(\text{sec})$$

The reactor volume is given by the expression

$$V_R = F \int_0^x \frac{dx}{r} \qquad (9\text{-A1})$$

The flow rate is

$$F = \left(\frac{(0.05)(1)(0.10)(14.7)}{(10.732)(671.7)}\right)(48) + \left(\frac{(0.05)(1)(0.9)(14.7)}{(10.732)(671.7)}\right)(32)$$
$$= 0.003426 \text{ lb/sec}$$

$$n_{0,O_3} = \frac{\dfrac{(0.05)(1)(0.1)(14.7)}{(10.732)(671.7)}}{0.003426} = 0.002976 \text{ lb mole per lb of feed}$$

For each mole of O_3 converted, $\frac{3}{2}$ moles of O_2 is formed. Initially there is 0.02977 total mole per lb of feed. At the point where x moles of O_3 per lb of feed have decomposed, the total moles per pound of feed is

$$n_t = n_0 + \tfrac{1}{2}x$$

The concentration of O_3 is

$$(O_3) = \frac{n_{0,O_3} - x}{n_t(RT/P)}$$

The rate of reaction is then

$$r = \frac{1.378(n_{0,O_3} - x)^2}{(n_0 + \frac{1}{2}x)^2(RT/P)^2} \qquad \text{lb mole/(ft}^3\text{)(sec)} \qquad (9\text{-A2})$$

Substitution of Eq. (9-A2) in Eq. (9-A1) gives

$$V_R = F \int_0^x \frac{dx}{\dfrac{(1.378)(n_{0,O_3} - x)^2}{(n_0 + \frac{1}{2}x)^2(RT/P)^2}} \qquad (9\text{-A3})$$

$$= \frac{F(RT)^2}{(1.378)(P)^2} \int_0^x \frac{(n_0 + \frac{1}{2}x)^2}{(n_{0,O_3} - x)^2} dx$$

Let $n_{0,O_3} = a = 0.002976$ lb mole of O_3 per lb of feed

$\quad n_0 = b = 0.02976$ total mole per lb of feed

$\quad \frac{1}{2} = c = 0.5$

$\quad x = 0.002976/2 = 0.001488$

$$\frac{(b + cx)^2}{(a - x)^2} = \frac{b^2}{(a - x)^2} + \frac{2bcx}{(a - x)^2} + \frac{c^2x^2}{(a - x)^2}$$

(1) $\displaystyle\int \frac{b^2}{(a - x)^2} dx = b^2 \left[\frac{1}{a - x} \right]_0^x$

(2) $\displaystyle\int \frac{2bcx}{(a - x)^2} dx = 2bc \left[\ln |a - x| + \frac{a}{a - x} \right]_0^x$

(3) $\displaystyle\int \frac{c^2x^2}{(a - x)^2} dx = -c^2 \left[(a - x) - 2a \ln |a - x| - \frac{a^2}{a - x} \right]_0^x$

$$b^2 = (2.976 \times 10^{-2})^2 = 8.857 \times 10^{-4}$$
$$a - x = 0.002976 = 0.001488 = 0.001488$$
$$(a - x)^2 = 2.214 \times 10^{-6}$$
$$2bcx = (2)(0.02976)(0.5)(0.001488) = 4.428 \times 10^{-5}$$
$$c^2x^2 = (0.25)(1.488 \times 10^{-3})^2 = 0.5535 \times 10^{-6}$$
$$2bc = (2)(0.02976)(0.5) = 0.02976$$
$$\ln |a - x| = \ln |0.001488| = -6.511$$
$$\ln |a| = \ln |0.002976| = -5.818$$
$$c^2 = 0.25$$
$$a^2 = 8.857 \times 10^{-6}$$

First integral:

$$= (8.857 \times 10^{-4}) \left[\frac{1}{1.488 \times 10^{-3}} - \frac{1}{2.976 \times 10^{-3}} \right]$$

$$= \frac{8.857 \times 10^{-4}}{2.976 \times 10^{-3}}$$

$$= 2.976 \times 10^{-1}$$

Second integral:

$$= (2.976 \times 10^{-2}) \left[-6.511 + 5.818 + \frac{2.976 \times 10^{-3}}{1.488 \times 10^{-3}} - \frac{2.976 \times 10^{-3}}{2.976 \times 10^{-3}} \right]$$
$$= (2.976 \times 10^{-2})[0.307]$$
$$= 0.9136 \times 10^{-2}$$

Third integral:

$$= -0.25 \left[0.001488 - 0.002976 - (5.952 \times 10^{-3})(-6.511 + 5.818) \right.$$
$$\left. - \left(\frac{8.857 \times 10^{-6}}{1.488 \times 10^{-3}} - \frac{8.857 \times 10^{-6}}{2.976 \times 10^{-3}} \right) \right]$$
$$= -0.25[-1.488 \times 10^{-3} + 4.125 \times 10^{-3} - 2.976 \times 10^{-3}]$$
$$= 8.48 \times 10^{-5}$$

Equation (9-A3) may then be written as

$$V_R = \frac{(0.003426)(10.732 \times 671.7)^2}{(1.378)(14.7)^2} (0.2976 + 0.009136 + 0.000085)$$
$$V_R = 18.3 \text{ ft}^3$$

or
$$L = 18.3 \text{ ft} \qquad \text{for unit cross section}$$

Complex Rate Equations

Actually most reaction-rate equations cannot be written as simply as Eq. (9-7). Complexity is to be expected because it is rather improbable that all reactions will be simple unions and separations of molecules. A good example of a complex reaction is the homogeneous reaction between H_2 and Br_2 to give HBr. The simple expression for the reaction is

$$\frac{d(\text{HBr})}{d\theta} = k_c(\text{H}_2)(\text{Br}_2) - k_c'(\text{HBr})^2 \qquad (9\text{-}22)$$

The experimentally verified expression, however, in the temperature range from 400 to 600°F is

$$\frac{d(\text{HBr})}{d\theta} = \frac{k_{c_1}(\text{H}_2)(\text{Br}_2)^{\frac{1}{2}}}{1 + k_{c_2}[(\text{HBr})/(\text{Br}_2)]} \qquad (9\text{-}23)$$

The complexities of reaction-rate equations stem from the complex steps in the formation of the product. In the present case, instead of a simple combination of H_2 and Br_2, there is a series of reactions involving H and Br. A summary of those reactions to show net rate gives Eq. (9-23). Generally speaking, the complex reaction-rate equations result from intermediate species being formed in the transformation from reactants to products.

Arrhenius Equation

In the treatment of reaction-rate problems it is often necessary to interpolate or extrapolate values for the rate constant as functions of temperature. The Arrhenius equation, used for such data treatment, is

$$k = Ae^{-E/RT} \tag{9-24}$$

It may be written in the logarithm form as

$$\ln k - \ln A = -\frac{E}{RT} \tag{9-25}$$

If Eq. (9-25) is differentiated with respect to temperature, it yields

$$\frac{d \ln k}{dT} = \frac{E}{RT^2} \tag{9-26}$$

which is another convenient way of relating the change in the specific reaction-rate constant to the change in temperature. A and E are taken as constant over small temperature ranges. E is the so-called "activation energy" for the reaction under consideration. Values for both E and A may be obtained from rate data for two different temperatures.

Example 9-B. The rate equation for the reaction

$$H_2 + Cl_2 \rightarrow 2HCl$$

may be given as

$$r = k_c(H_2)(Cl_2)$$

At 230°C the value of k is 0.17 liter/(mole)(sec), whereas at 240°C it is 0.25 liter/(mole)(sec). What is its value at 300°C?

Solution. The Arrhenius equation can be applied.

At 230°C:
$$\ln (0.17) - \ln A = -\frac{E}{(1.987)(503.2)} \tag{9-B1}$$

At 240°C:
$$\ln (0.25) - \ln A = -\frac{E}{(1.987)(513.2)} \tag{9-B2}$$

Equations (9-B1) and (9-B2) may be solved simultaneously to obtain values of A and E as follows:

$$A = (6.7 \times 10^7)(\text{liter})/(\text{mole})(\text{sec})$$
$$E = 19{,}800 \text{ cal}$$

The other form of the Arrhenius equation is then

$$k = (6.7 \times 10^7)e^{-19{,}800/RT}$$

At 300°C: $k = 1.9 \text{ liters}/(\text{mole})(\text{sec})$

Heterogeneous Reactions

The rate equations discussed above are for homogeneous or single-phase reactions. Not only must the chemical engineer learn to cope with chemical kinetics in homogeneous reactions, but also he must deal with reactions in heterogeneous systems. Of special interest in heterogeneous reactions are the catalyzed reactions for which the catalytic agent is a solid phase, and the fluid phase is a gas. Catalytic cracking of hydrocarbons falls into that category. In cracking, the solid-phase catalyst can be a pelletized fixed-bed packing with particle sizes in the range from $\frac{1}{8}$ to $\frac{3}{4}$ in. in diameter, or a fluidized solid having a particle size in the range of 40 microns (i.e., millionths of a meter) or 0.0016 in. In cracking, the solid-phase catalyst can be a silica-alumina mass. In other solid-phase catalysis the active catalyst can be a surface coating on an inert carrier such as diatomaceous earth. The total solid phase in any case is referred to as the catalyst mass.

The rate equations for heterogeneous catalysis are very complex because of all the factors that can contribute to the rate. In the general case there is the problem of diffusion of reactants to the surface of the catalyst, adsorption of reactants, surface reaction, desorption of products, and diffusion of products. All these steps are in contrast to the more simple case of a homogeneous reaction for which all the surface-associated steps are absent.

10

Fixation of Nitrogen

Replenishment of nitrogen in the soil has long been recognized as a major requirement in successful agricultural operations. Over a major part of history that replenishment has been marginal and has been accomplished through the application of natural organic fertilizers. Even today in the less industrialized countries the replenishment is inadequate. In industrialized countries the situation is improving, because means are available for economically manufacturing and distributing fixed nitrogen, which is nitrogen in compounds in contrast to free nitrogen in the atmosphere. An organic nitrogen fertilizer requires that the farmer pay about 50 cents or more per pound of available nitrogen. He obtains valuable trace elements and mulching material in that purchase, but even so he is more inclined to pay about 10 cents/lb for fixed nitrogen in the form of ammonium nitrate. Agricultural operations thus provide a major market for fixed nitrogen. About 4 million short tons of nitrogen in fixed form is available annually in the United States. About 80% of this quantity is obtained by synthesis, 11% from imports, and 9% from by-product and waste nitrogen. About 75% of the nitrogen produced by synthesis is used in fertilizer, and the remainder goes to miscellaneous industrial uses.

Fixation Processes for Nitrogen

With such a large and growing market for fixed nitrogen, it is apparent that the fixation process continues to be of major interest to the chemical engineer. Early work in nitrogen fixation centered about the arc process

$$N_2(g) + O_2(g) \rightleftharpoons 2NO(g) \qquad \Delta H_{25°C} = 21,500 \text{ cal} \qquad (10\text{-}1)$$

The cyanamide process also was of early importance, and the reaction may be written as

$$CaC_2(s) + N_2(g) \rightleftharpoons CaCN_2(s) + C(s) \qquad \begin{aligned} \Delta H_{1100°C} = \\ -68,500 \text{ cal} \dagger \end{aligned} \qquad (10\text{-}2)$$

In the arc process, air was passed through an electric arc with resultant need for large quantities of inexpensive electrical energy. The process did not have continuing commercial interest in the United States because of the energy requirements. It was used in Norway after 1904 but today is obsolescent.

The cyanamide process started in the United States in 1909, and still is in use today. As a source of fixed nitrogen for agricultural needs it has been replaced largely by the synthetic ammonia process. In that process nitrogen and hydrogen are reacted according to the equation

$$\tfrac{1}{2}N_2(g) + \tfrac{3}{2}H_2(g) \rightleftharpoons NH_3(g) \qquad \Delta H_{500°C} = -12,944 \text{ cal} \qquad (10\text{-}3)$$

The ammonia processes used today are essentially outgrowths of the Haber process developed in Germany before World War I and put into production in 1913.

Conditions for Ammonia Synthesis

In the Haber type of process, purified nitrogen and hydrogen are passed over an iron catalyst at temperatures in the neighborhood of 500°C and at pressures ranging from 1500 to 15,000 psi (100 to 1000 atm). Figure 10-1 shows the equilibrium percentage of NH_3 as a function of pressure for several temperatures. A consideration of this plot alone would suggest a low temperature, say less than 200°C, for greatest yield from the reaction. If the process were operated at 200°C, the small change in equilibrium yields above about 6000 psia (400 atm) indicates that pressures higher than that value would not be worthwhile. Operating conditions, however, cannot be directly derived from a considera-

† R. N. Shreve, "The Chemical Process Industries," p. 397, McGraw-Hill Book Company, Inc., New York, 1956.

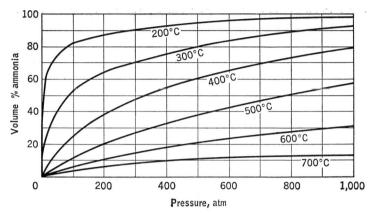

FIG. 10-1. Equilibrium per cent of ammonia for the reaction $N_2 +$ $3H_2 \rightleftharpoons 2NH_3$ with an initial stoichiometric mixture. [*From A. T. Larson, The Ammonia Equilibrium at High Pressures, J. Am. Chem. Soc.*, **46**, 367 (1924); *with permission.*]

tion of equilibrium data alone. It is necessary also to include rate effects, along with other factors, and finally the engineer arrives at the most economical process design. For the reaction of nitrogen and hydrogen at 200°C, the rate is low, and, even though equilibrium yields would be high, the process would not be so practicable as one at a higher temperature. At 500°C, yields would be smaller but satisfactory, whereas rates would be much higher than at 200°C.

Equilibrium in Ammonia Synthesis

Tabulated values are available for the equilibrium constant for the reaction

$$\tfrac{1}{2}N_2(g) + \tfrac{3}{2}H_2(g) \rightleftharpoons NH_3(g) \tag{10-4}$$

Table 10-1 gives the values for the constants in the functional relationship of K_P expressed in atm^{-1} and T in degrees Kelvin. More recent work has extended the field of knowledge to 3500 atm for the temperatures of 400 and 450°C as shown in Table 10-2. It should be noted, in these tables, that K_P is not a true equilibrium constant as defined in Eq. (8-9), because it is a ratio of partial pressures and not of activities. It may be used, however, in making useful computations over a wide range of conditions in the synthesis of NH_3.

TABLE 10-1. COEFFICIENTS FOR THE EMPIRICAL EQUILIBRIUM CONSTANT
EQUATION FOR THE REACTION $\frac{1}{2}N_2(g) + \frac{3}{2}H_2(g) \rightleftharpoons NH_3(g)$ †

$$K_P = \frac{p_{NH_3}}{(p_{N_2})^{\frac{1}{2}}(p_{H_2})^{\frac{3}{2}}} \quad atm^{-1}$$

$$\log K_P = \frac{\alpha}{T} + \beta \log T + \gamma T + \delta T^2 + I$$

$$\alpha = +2074.8°K \qquad \beta = -2.4943$$

Pressure, atm	$\gamma \times 10^5$, °K^{-1}	$\delta \times 10^7$, °K^{-2}	I
10	0	1.856	1.993
30	−3.4	1.856	2.021
50	−12.56	1.856	2.090
100	−12.56	1.856	2.113
300	−12.56	1.8564	2.206
600	−108.56	1.8564	3.059
1000	−268.33	1.8564	4.473

† A. T. Larson and R. L. Dodge, The Ammonia Equilibrium, *J. Am. Chem. Soc.*, **45**, 2918 (1923), and A. T. Larson, The Ammonia Equilibrium at High Pressures, *J. Am. Chem. Soc.*, **46**, 367 (1924); with permission. K_P represents an empirical equilibrium constant expressed in partial pressures in contradistinction to K which involves activities. Temperature is expressed in degrees Kelvin. The initial mixture of nitrogen and hydrogen was in stoichiometric proportions.

Rate of Catalytic Reaction between Nitrogen and Hydrogen

The reaction between N_2 and H_2 to give ammonia is catalyzed by iron in combination with oxides such as Al_2O_3 and K_2O. The added oxides are called promoters† and enhance the activity of the main catalyst. A doubly promoted iron catalyst might contain 2 to 3% Al_2O_3 and the same amount of K_2O. In the catalysis of the reaction between N_2 and H_2 to give NH_3, an applicable rate equation is

$$\frac{1}{2}\frac{d(N_{NH_3})}{d\theta} = k_1 W p_{N_2}\left(\frac{p_{H_2}^3}{p_{NH_3}^2}\right)^n - k_2 W \left(\frac{p_{NH_3}^2}{p_{H_2}^3}\right)^{1-n} \qquad (10\text{-}5)$$

† A promoter enhances the action of a catalyst by physical or chemical effects. In a reduced iron catalyst for ammonia synthesis, Al_2O_3 helps in giving increased surface area and maintaining that area during use. In an iron catalyst for ammonia synthesis K_2O does not affect surface area but enhances the catalytic activity at elevated pressures (100 atm), possibly by accelerating the desorption of ammonia.

TABLE 10-2. EFFECT OF PRESSURE ON THE EMPIRICAL EQUILIBRIUM
CONSTANT FOR THE REACTION $\frac{1}{2}N_2(g) + \frac{3}{2}H_2(g) \rightleftharpoons NH_3(g)$[†]

$$K_P = \frac{p_{NH_3}}{(p_{N_2})^{\frac{1}{2}}(p_{H_2})^{\frac{3}{2}}}$$

Temperature, °C	Pressure, atm	K_P, atm^{-1}
400	1000	0.06136
400	1500	0.1384
400	2000	0.2977
400	2500	0.7864
400	3000	1.2543
400	3500	1.6283
450	1000	0.02496
450	1500	0.06962
450	1650	0.09404
450	2000	0.1337
450	3500	1.0751

† L. J. Winchester and B. F. Dodge, The Chemical Equilibrium of the
Ammonia Synthesis Reaction at High Temperatures and Extreme Pressures,
AIChE Journal, **2**, 431 (1956); with permission. Partial pressures are
expressed in atmospheres. A stoichiometric mixture of nitrogen and hydrogen was initially introduced.

The quantities in Eq. (10-5) are defined† as follows:

N_{NH_3} = mole fraction of NH_3
θ = time
k_1 = forward rate constant
k_2 = reverse rate constant
W = volume of catalyst mass
p_{N_2} = partial pressure of nitrogen
p_{H_2} = partial pressure of hydrogen
p_{NH_3} = partial pressure of ammonia

The value of n appears to be close to 0.7. In earlier work by
Emmett and Kummer,‡ n was taken as 0.5. Values of k_1 and k_2
can be derived from experimental data but are not found to be
constant because the equation does not exactly describe the

† R. Brill, The Rate Equation of Ammonia Synthesis on Iron Type
Catalysts of Different Composition, *J. Chem. Phys.*, **19**, 1047 (1951).
‡ P. H. Emmett and J. T. Kummer, Kinetics of Ammonia Synthesis,
Ind. Eng. Chem., **35**, 677 (1943).

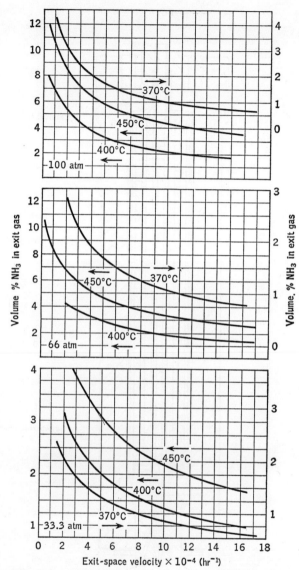

FIG. 10-2. Rate of ammonia synthesis from a 3:1 volume mixture of hydrogen and nitrogen. [*Reprinted from P. H. Emmett and J. T. Kummer, Kinetics of Ammonia Synthesis, Ind. Eng. Chem.*, **35**, 677 (1943). *Copyright 1943 by the American Chemical Society and reprinted by permission of the copyright owner.*]

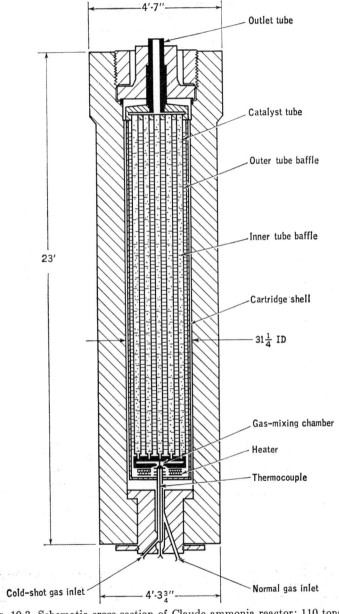

Fig. 10-3. Schematic cross section of Claude ammonia reactor: 110 tons of NH₃ per day. [*From H. L. Thompson, Pierre Guillaumeron, and N. C. Updegraff, Ammonia Synthesis at 1,000 Atmospheres, Chem. Eng. Progr.,* **48** (9), 468–475 (1952).]

kinetics of ammonia synthesis, and further studies are in order. Such values do furnish, however, a useful guide to industrial reaction rates.

In Fig. 10-2, information from the work of Emmett and Kummer is shown. The percentage yields of NH_3 as a function of hourly space velocity† and pressure are given. An analysis of these rate curves allows evaluation of the specific rate constants in Eq. (10-5).

In the operation of commercial reactors for the manufacture of ammonia, such as that shown diagrammatically in Fig. 10-3, the pressures vary considerably from process to process, but the temperatures do not. Generally speaking, the pressure is in the range of 1500 to 15,000 psi, and the temperature is about 500°C. An iron catalyst is used that is either singly or doubly promoted. Percentage conversion in a reactor will be in the range of 10 to 40% but is usually around 20%. After the gases leave the reactor they are cooled, and the liquid is separated from the gases in a separator. Liquid NH_3 is sent to storage, and the gas phase is recycled to the process at a point upstream from the catalytic reactor.

Manufacture of Gases for Ammonia Synthesis

Hydrogen for the ammonia reaction is usually obtained by processing natural gas by one of several available processes. Nitrogen is prepared by the low-temperature fractionation of air. Oxygen is obtained as a by-product of that fractionation. It can be used in the manufacture of hydrogen from natural gas, sold as tonnage oxygen, or wasted.

Several processes are available for preparation of hydrogen. The older procedures are its recovery from water gas, producer gas, or coke-oven gas. Representative compositions of these gases are given in Table 10-3. Electrolysis of water also has accounted for a significant proportion of hydrogen production. Main interest, however, is in the processing of CH_4, or other low-molecular-weight hydrocarbons of the same series, to yield H_2.

† Space velocity represents the number of cubic feet of gas, as measured at 32°F and 14.7 psi, flowing per unit time per cubic foot of reactor volume, which includes the catalyst mass and the fluid passing by it. The unit of time is usually one hour. As can be seen, the volume unit chosen cancels out and does not affect the value of space velocity.

TABLE 10-3. COMPOSITION OF FUEL GASES†
(In volume per cent)

Constituent	Water gas	Producer gas	Coke-oven gas
CO	38.3	25.3	6.3
CO_2	5.5	5.4	1.8
N_2	2.8	55.2	3.4
O_2	0.2	0.5	0.2
H_2	52.8	13.2	53.0
CH_4	0.4	0.4	31.6
C_2H_4	—	—	2.7
C_6H_6	—	—	1.0

† J. H. Perry (ed.), "Chemical Engineers' Handbook," 3d ed., p. 1577, McGraw-Hill Book Company, Inc., New York, 1950; with permission.

Special mention should be made of the partial-oxidation reactions involving hydrocarbons and the steam-methane reaction. In the partial-oxidation reactions, gaseous hydrocarbons, oil, or coal may be the raw material used. Natural gas is used most commonly, and, because it is mainly methane, the chemical reaction is essentially

$$CH_4(g) + \tfrac{1}{2}O_2(g) \rightleftharpoons CO(g) + 2H_2(g) \qquad \Delta H_{25°C} = -8527 \text{ cal} \tag{10-6}$$

This process is becoming of greater interest because of the decreased amount of gas to be handled when using relatively pure oxygen from the fractionation of air, and avoidance of the need for catalytic agents. The process is conducted at a pressure of about 325 psia and a temperature of 2000°F.

The steam-methane reaction

$$CH_4(g) + H_2O(g) \rightleftharpoons CO(g) + 3H_2(g) \qquad \Delta H_{1100°C} = 108,000 \text{ cal} \tag{10-7}$$

is of main interest but is receiving active competition from the partial-oxidation process. Equilibrium data for the reaction are given in Table 10-4. For a reasonable reaction rate, catalysis is required. Fortunately the nickel catalyst, which is supported on an inert material, is not easily poisoned or inactivated by saturated hydrocarbons. Noncatalytic reactions such as those of partial oxidation have an attraction, nevertheless, because of the probability of lower maintenance costs.

TABLE 10-4. EQUILIBRIUM CONSTANTS FOR THE
STEAM-METHANE REACTION†

$$K_P = \frac{(p_{CO})(p_{H_2})^3}{(p_{CH_4})(p_{H_2O})}$$

t, °F	K_P, atm²
980	0.033
1340	27.3
1500	260
1550	450
1600	870
1700	2640
1800	4710

† R. M. Reed, The Commercial Production of Pure Hydrogen from Hydrocarbons and Steam, *Trans. AIChE*, **41**, 453 (1945); with permission. Partial pressures are expressed in atmospheres.

Water-shift Reaction

In each method, except the electrolysis of water, the impure gas produced requires removal of CO because of its poisoning effect on catalysts. This is removed by the so-called "water-shift reaction." This reaction is important, and its successful application is a major factor in the operation of economical ammonia processes. It may be written as

$$CO(g) + H_2O(g) \rightleftharpoons H_2(g) + CO_2(g) \qquad \Delta H_{371°C} = 9170 \text{ cal}$$
$$(10\text{-}8)$$

Empirically developed equilibrium constants have been tabulated by Reed and are shown in Table 10-5. The formation of CO_2 is favored by low temperatures, but the rate decreases as the temperature decreases. It is necessary to operate at temperatures

TABLE 10-5. EMPIRICAL EQUILIBRIUM CONSTANTS
FOR THE WATER-SHIFT REACTION†

$$K_P = \frac{(p_{CO_2})(p_{H_2})}{(p_{CO})(p_{H_2O})} = (0.0202) \, e^{7350/(°F+400)}$$

t, °F	K_P	t, °F	K_P
260	1410	752	12
440	113	800	9.1
620	27	842	7.5
662	21	932	5.0

† R. M. Reed, The Commercial Production of Pure Hydrogen from Hydrocarbons and Steam, *Trans. AIChE*, **41**, 453 (1945); with permission.

in the region of 800°F and in the presence of a catalyst to obtain satisfactory rates and conversions.

Bridger, Gernes, and Thompson have reported results obtained in studies of catalysts for the water-shift reaction. Results for laboratory tests are shown in Fig. 10-4, and Fig. 10-5 shows the

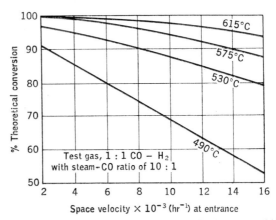

FIG. 10-4. The per cent conversion of CO to CO_2 in the water-shift reaction at atmospheric pressure. [*Reprinted from G. L. Bridger, D. C. Gernes, and H. L. Thompson, Chem. Eng. Progr.*, **44**, 363 (1948); *with permission.*]

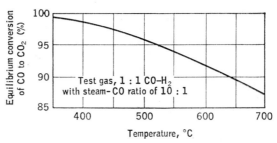

FIG. 10-5. Equilibrium conversion of CO to CO_2 in the water-shift reaction at atmospheric pressure. [*Reprinted from G. L. Bridger, D. C. Gernes, and H. L. Thompson, Chem. Eng. Progr.*, **44**, 363 (1948); *with permission.*]

equilibrium conversion of CO for the same range of conditions. Operation was at atmospheric pressure. The composition of the catalyst, reported as oxides, is given in Table 10-6. It was in the form of pellets having diameters of 0.3 in. and lengths of 0.5 in., and the external surface area was 1.7 ft^2 per lb of catalyst. In actual plant use, performance of the reactor is not so efficient as that of the laboratory facility because of channeling and less satisfactory temperature control.

TABLE 10-6. COMPOSITION OF A CATALYST FOR THE
WATER-SHIFT REACTION†

Constituent	wt %	Constituent	wt %
Fe_2O_3	53.8	SO_3	0.5
MgO	17.3	SiO_2	1.0
CrO_3	4.6	CaO	0.5
K_2O	2.2	H_2O (110°C)	2.1
Al_2O_3	0.3	CO_2	14.3
Na_2O	0.3	Ignition loss including moisture	21.9

† G. C. Bridger, D. C. Gernes, and H. L. Thompson, Development, Production, and Performance of Water-Gas Conversion Catalyst, *Chem. Eng. Progr.*, **44**, 363 (1948); with permission.

The water-shift reaction opens the possibility of producing hydrogen gas from coke, which contains almost no hydrogen. Partial oxidation of carbon with oxygen gas results in CO in accordance with the reaction

$$C(s) + \tfrac{1}{2}O_2(g) \rightleftharpoons CO(g) \qquad (10\text{-}9)$$

The resulting CO gas can then be subjected to the water-shift reaction to produce a mixture of H_2 and CO_2.

Final Purification of Hydrogen

The gases resulting from the water-shift reaction contain H_2, CO_2, and H_2O as the main constituents with small amounts of CO and the original hydrocarbon, such as CH_4. The other constituents must be removed from the H_2 before it can be used catalytically with N_2 to make ammonia.

Purification is begun by removing CO_2 by absorbing it in an aqueous solution of monoethanolamine. To give a low residual CO_2 content, the process is conducted under pressure at room temperature with aqueous solutions containing up to 30% of the amine. Pressures up to 250 psia are used, and the absorption is accomplished in a tower with the gases passing upward counter-current to a descending liquid stream, as indicated in Fig. 10-6. Less concentrated solutions of monoethanolamine and low operating pressures tend to leave some CO_2 unabsorbed. The reaction is merely one between an acidic substance, CO_2, and a basic

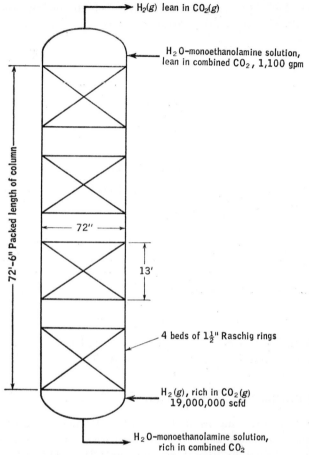

FIG. 10-6. Hydrogen purification by countercurrent absorption of CO_2 in monoethonolamine solution. (*The Fluor Corporation, Ltd.*)

substance, monoethanolamine. From a simplified point of view the reaction may be written as

$$CO_2 + H_2O + 2HOCH_2CH_2NH_2$$
$$\rightleftharpoons (HOCH_2CH_2NH_3)_2^{++} + CO_3^{=} \quad (10\text{-}10)$$

With sufficient CO_2 the reaction becomes

$$CO_2 + H_2O + HOCH_2CH_2NH_2$$
$$\rightleftharpoons (HOCH_2CH_2NH_3)^+ + HCO_3^- \quad (10\text{-}11)$$

TABLE 10-7. COST OF AMMONIA WITH NATURAL GAS
AS SOURCE OF HYDROGEN[a]
(Manufacturing costs in dollars per ton of NH_3)

	Tons per stream-day	
	100	200
Capital investment for total plant	$3,950,000	$6,843,000
Materials:		
Natural-gas feed, 31.2¢ per 1000 std cu ft (30¢ per million Btu)	8.11	8.11
Shift catalyst, 72¢ per lb	0.22	0.22
Synthesis catalyst, 60¢ per lb	0.30	0.30
Caustic, 3¢ per lb	0.24	0.24
Monoethanolamine, 26¢ per lb	0.08	0.08
Lube oil, 80¢ per gal	0.40	0.40
	$ 9.35	$ 9.35
Utilities:		
Fuel gas, 30¢ per million Btu	6.60	6.60
Electricity, 0.8¢ per kwhr	0.86	0.86
Treated water, 13¢ per 1000 gal	0.14	0.14
Raw water, 5¢ per 1000 gal	0.23	0.23
	$ 7.83	$ 7.83
Other operating expenses:		
Operating labor, $2.25 per man-hr + 22% payroll burden[b]	4.85[c]	2.43[c]
Maintenance, 4% of capital investment[d]	4.55	3.94
Plant general, 40% of total labor[e]	3.03	1.92
	$12.43	$ 8.29
Fixed charges:		
Depreciation, 10%	11.38	9.86
Taxes, interest, insurance, 6%	6.83	5.92
	$18.21	$15.78
Sum of variable manufacturing costs	$47.82	$41.25

[a] B. S. Duff, Economics of Ammonia Manufacture from Several Raw
Materials, *Chem. Eng. Progr.*, **51**, 12-J (1955); with permission.

[b] Payroll burden covers vacation, insurance, benefits.

[c] Adjusted for 95% operating factor.

[d] Maintenance is 60% labor, 40% material.

[e] Typical, including nonoperating service and administrative personnel
up to and including plant manager.

Other basic solutions such as an aqueous solution of Na_2CO_3 and K_2CO_3 may be used. Also di- and triethanolamines have application but are more easily oxidized than the monoethanolamine. Monoethanolamine solution is being used more and more, relative to carbonate solutions, because of greater absorption capacity and the ease of regeneration by merely boiling at atmospheric pressure. It is essentially a nonvolatile variant of ammonia in the absorption of the acidic CO_2.

After most of the CO_2 has been removed by a process such as just described and residual CO_2 is absorbed in a final caustic wash, the water-shift gas is dried and passed on to the final purification. Liquid nitrogen can be used in that process. Any residual CO, CH_4, or other gases with boiling points higher than that of nitrogen are condensed, and the hydrogen, with a small amount of nitrogen picked up in the purification step, is mixed with the proper proportion of purified nitrogen before the high-pressure synthesis of ammonia.

Ammonia Manufacturing Costs

The manufacture of ammonia is a very competitive enterprise. A review of its economics gives a better understanding of the various factors that are important in the development of a profitable chemical process. Duff has summarized the economics in 1955 for different sources of hydrogen and excerpts of his

TABLE 10-8. COMPARISON OF COSTS OF AMMONIA USING HYDROGEN
FROM DIFFERENT SOURCES[†]
(Summation of manufacturing costs in dollars per ton of NH_3)

Source of hydrogen	Tons/stream-day	
	100	200
Natural gas	$47.82	$41.25
Fuel oil	50.93	44.16
Coal	53.38	46.51
Coke-oven gas	40.96	35.01
Catalytic-reformer gas[‡]	34.34	29.34

[†] B. S. Duff, Economics of Ammonia Manufacture from Several Raw Materials, *Chem. Eng. Progr.*, **51**, 12-J (1955); with permission.
[‡] Obtained from petroleum refinery operations.

presentation are shown in Tables 10-7 and 10-8. The data for manufacturing costs can be compared with the current selling price of ammonia by noting that the manufacturing cost when natural gas was taken as a source of hydrogen was approximately 65% of the selling price. The difference stems from the charges for research, administration, selling, and distribution, as well as the allowance for gross profit. The challenges to the chemical engineer in improving process economics are apparent.

11

Nitric Acid

Nitric acid is used mainly in the manufacture of inorganic and organic nitrogen compounds and as an oxidant for fuels used in missile propulsion. In inorganic reactions, the manufacture of ammonium nitrate from ammonia and nitric acid is the most important process. In organic reactions nitric acid is used to make both nitrate and nitro compounds. Nitrate compounds of importance are glyceryl trinitrate (nitroglycerine) and nitrocellulose; an easily recognized nitro compound is trinitrotoluene, commonly known as TNT. Organic nitrates are distinguished from the nitro compounds by their structure, the former having the oxygen attached to the carbon, and the latter having the nitrogen attached to the carbon; for example,

$$\begin{array}{cccc} & | & & | \\ -\!\!\!&C\!-\!O\!-\!N\!=\!\!=\!O & \qquad -\!\!\!&C\!-\!N\!=\!\!=\!O \\ & | \quad \diagdown & & | \quad \diagdown \\ & \quad O & & \quad O \end{array}$$

Organic nitrate   Nitro compound

Ammonia Oxidation

Before the use of the Haber type of process for ammonia manufacture, nitric acid ordinarily was made from Chilean sodium nitrate according to the reaction

$$NaNO_3(s) + H_2SO_4(l) \rightarrow NaHSO_4(s) + HNO_3(l) \quad (11\text{-}1)$$

Today, however, NH_3 is so economically manufactured that the

124

reaction of main commercial interest in the preparation of nitric acid is

$$4NH_3(g) + 5O_2(g) \rightleftharpoons 4NO(g) \quad \begin{cases} \Delta H_{25°C} = -216,547 \text{ cal} \\ + 6H_2O(g) \quad \Delta F^°_{25°C} = -229,323 \text{ cal} \end{cases} \quad (11\text{-}2)$$

A gas mixture containing 1 volume of ammonia to 7.5 volumes of air is passed through a multilayered platinum gauze, as shown schematically in Fig. 11-1. Even though the reaction is exothermic, the gases just before passing through the gauze will have been heated to 300 to 400°C. The preheating is accomplished by

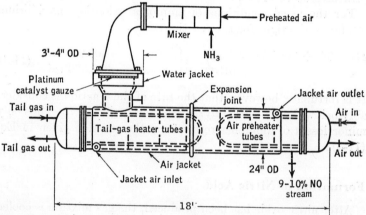

FIG. 11-1. Schematic diagram of ammonia oxidizer and heat exchanger: 60 tons of HNO₃ per day. (*The Fluor Corporation, Ltd.*)

mixing heated air with nonheated ammonia immediately before the gases enter the oxidizer unit. If the ammonia were preheated, it would partially decompose with resultant loss of ammonia, according to the reaction

$$NH_3(g) \rightleftharpoons \tfrac{3}{2}H_2(g) + \tfrac{1}{2}N_2(g) \qquad (11\text{-}3)$$

If the mixture of air and ammonia entering the gauze pad is at 300°C, a temperature of about 1000°C is reached as the result of the exothermic reaction described by Eq. (11-2). The pressure is either atmospheric or about 100 psia. The higher pressure is used if the process is to produce 61 to 65% nitric acid, rather than 50% acid.† The reaction time is the shortest for any known

† G. B. Taylor, T. H. Chilton, and S. L. Handforth, Manufacture of Nitric Acid by the Oxidation of Ammonia, *Ind. Eng. Chem.*, **23**, 860 (1931).

contact catalysis and is about 0.0001 sec.† For the conditions described, about 70 lb of ammonia can be oxidized per day per troy ounce of platinum catalyst. The loss of platinum amounts to about 7% per year.

The temperature of about 1000°C in the vicinity of the gauze catalyst is needed to obtain the desired rate. Because the reaction is exothermic, increasing temperature, in accordance with the van't Hoff equation, Eq. (8-16), decreases the percentage conversion at equilibrium. Calculation shows, nevertheless, that an equilibrium conversion of better than 99% is possible for temperatures up to 1500°C.

For the usual conditions of ammonia oxidation, equilibrium lies far to the right for the reaction:

$$4NH_3(g) + 3O_2(g) \rightarrow 2N_2(g) \quad \begin{cases} \Delta H_{25°C} = -302,950 \text{ cal} \\ \Delta F^\circ_{25°C} = -312,060 \text{ cal} \end{cases} \quad (11\text{-}4)$$
$$+ 6H_2O(g)$$

It is fortunate, however, that the rate of the reaction is considerably below that of the catalyzed reaction to give NO. Thus only minor losses of ammonia result from the reaction given in Eq. (11-4).

Formation of Nitric Acid

After nitric oxide has been produced, the gas mixture is cooled to about 30°C. At this temperature NO reacts with excess O_2 in the gas mixture in accordance with the equation

$$2NO(g) + O_2(g) \rightleftharpoons 2NO_2(g) \qquad \Delta H_{25°C} = -27,280 \text{ cal} \quad (11\text{-}5)$$

This reaction is slow, however, at atmospheric pressure and time must be allowed for it to proceed. As shown by Eq. (11-5), the reaction is exothermic, and a low temperature gives a favorable equilibrium state. A compromise is necessary between a low temperature with slow reaction but good equilibrium yield and a higher temperature requiring less time but giving poorer equilibrium yield. Operation at higher pressure would have the effect of increasing both rate and equilibrium yield, and so it offers advantages, which are partly counterbalanced by increased difficulties in pressure operations with corrosive substances.

After cooling, the gas is passed through a series of small tanks

† G. B. Taylor, Oxidation of Ammonia, *Ind. Eng. Chem.*, **19**, 1250 (1927).

with coolers between them. The tanks allow time for oxidation of NO, and the intercoolers remove the heat of reaction and keep the temperature low. Next the gases are passed through a series of absorption towers, each about 10 ft in diameter by 50 ft high, lined with acid-proof materials. Here the gases meet in counter-current flow a solution of nitric acid. The NO_2 reacts with H_2O in the solution as follows:

$$3NO_2(g) + H_2O(l) \rightleftharpoons 2HNO_3(60\% \text{ soln}) + NO(g)$$
$$\Delta H = -28,800 \text{ cal} \quad (11\text{-}6)$$

The NO produced in this reaction may in turn react with excess O_2 in accordance with Eq. (11-5). Heat of reaction must also be removed during this absorption process.

At atmospheric pressure, the rate of the reaction shown in Eq. (11-5) is controlling. For a pressure of 100 psia, the reaction in Eq. (11-6) is controlling. In both cases, the reaction is best conducted at a temperature of less than 50°C for satisfactory yields.

For the operation at atmospheric pressure, 4 to 12 absorption towers in series† are used, with water entering the last of these towers and product acid leaving the first one. The last one or two towers are alkaline absorbers for residual NO_2 according to the reaction

$$2NO_2(g) + Na_2CO_3(aq) \rightarrow NaNO_3(aq) + NaNO_2(aq) + CO_2(g)$$
$$(11\text{-}7)$$

For a residence time of 40 sec per tower, eight towers operated at 40°C give 90% oxidation of NO to NO_2 and a recovery of 90% of the NO_2. An acid strength of about 48 wt % is achieved. Eleven towers give a recovery of about 95% of the NO_2 and an acid strength of 50%. If the latter results were to be attained at 25°C, only nine towers would be required. At 0°C five towers would give the same recovery but with 60% acid as the product. The equilibria are such that at 40°C it is not possible to obtain 60% acid.

In operation at atmospheric pressure, 25 tons of 50% acid per day can be manufactured, using 10 absorption towers in series where each tower has a diameter of 10 ft and a height of 50 ft.

† G. B. Taylor, T. H. Chilton, and S. L. Handforth, Manufacture of Nitric Acid by the Oxidation of Ammonia, *Ind. Eng. Chem.*, **23**, 860 (1931).

Operation at 100 psia gives a decreased capital cost because a single absorption column with a diameter of $5\frac{1}{4}$ ft and a height of 40 ft is adequate for production of 25 tons of 60% acid per day. Operation at higher pressures is in the region of diminishing economical returns as fabrication of thicker-walled vessels for the process is relatively more costly. The yield in the atmospheric plant from ammonia to acid is about 90% of theoretical, whereas in the pressure plant that yield or higher is obtained.

Concentrated Nitric Acid

If nitric acid having a concentration greater than 60 wt % is desired, concentration of the product from either the atmospheric- or higher-pressure manufacture must be effected. Nitric acid

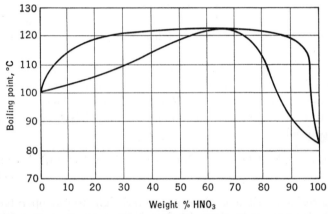

FIG. 11-2. Vapor-liquid equilibrium for the HNO_3-H_2O system at atmospheric pressure. [*Reprinted from Paul Pascal, Distillation Studies of Nitric Acid and Sulphuric-Nitric Acid Mixtures—II, Chem. Met. Eng.*, **25**, 1145 (1921); *with permission.*]

forms a constant-boiling mixture with water at 68% HNO_3 as is indicated in the equilibrium diagram of Fig. 11-2. Therefore, to obtain a more concentrated acid a breaking of the constant-boiling characteristic is required. This is accomplished by adding sulfuric acid to the mixture of nitric acid and water. The sulfuric acid effectively decreases the activity of water in the solution, and nitric acid of higher concentration can then be distilled from the mixture. Up to 99% nitric acid can be prepared in that manner.

Rate of Oxidation of NO

As noted, in the manufacture of nitric acid at atmospheric pressure, the rate of the reaction is controlled by the gas-phase oxidation of NO in accordance with Eq. (11-5). The reaction is essentially irreversible under the conditions of manufacture and is termolecular, or third-order, according to the equation

$$- \frac{d(\text{NO})}{d\theta} = k(\text{NO})^2(\text{O}_2) \tag{11-8}$$

It is one of the few reactions in which the rate decreases with increasing temperature. That phenomenon has been explained† by use of the equations

$$\text{NO}(g) + \text{O}_2(g) \rightleftharpoons \text{NO}_3(g) \qquad \text{rapidly achieved equilibrium} \tag{11-9}$$

$$\text{NO}_3(g) + \text{NO}(g) \underset{k_2}{\overset{k_1}{\rightleftharpoons}} \text{NO}_3 \cdot \text{NO}(g)$$
$$\text{rapidly achieved equilibrium} \tag{11-10}$$

$$\text{NO}_3 \cdot \text{NO}(g) + \text{NO}_2(g) \overset{k_3}{\rightarrow} 2\text{NO}(g) + \text{O}_2(g) + \text{NO}_2(g) \tag{11-11}$$

$$\text{NO}_3(g) + \text{NO}_2(g) \rightleftharpoons \text{N}_2\text{O}_5(g) \qquad \text{rapidly achieved equilibrium} \tag{11-12}$$

$$\text{NO}_3(g) + \text{NO}(g) \overset{k_5}{\rightarrow} 2\text{NO}_2(g) \tag{11-13}$$

$$\text{NO}_3 \cdot \text{NO}(g) + \text{NO}(g) \overset{k_6}{\rightarrow} 2\text{NO}_2(g) + \text{NO}(g) \tag{11-14}$$

$$K_9 = \frac{(\text{NO}_3)}{(\text{NO})(\text{O}_2)} \tag{11-15}$$

$$K_{12} = \frac{(\text{N}_2\text{O}_5)}{(\text{NO}_3)(\text{NO}_2)} \tag{11-16}$$

The species NO_3, $\text{NO}_3 \cdot \text{NO}$, and N_2O_5 are assumed to be present in trace concentrations not varying with time. An instantaneous material balance gives

$$\frac{d(\text{NO}_2)}{d\theta} = (\text{NO})^2(\text{O}_2)k_5K_9 \left[1 + \frac{k_6k_1(\text{NO})}{k_5[k_2 + k_3(\text{NO}_2) + k_6(\text{NO})]} \right] \tag{11-17}$$

At high partial pressures of NO_2, the last fractional term in Eq.

† J. C. Treacy and F. Daniels, Kinetic Study of the Oxidation of Nitric Oxide with Oxygen in the Pressure Range 1 to 20 mm, *J. Am. Chem. Soc.*, **77**, 2033 (1955).

(11-17) becomes small, and the reaction may be written as

$$\frac{d(NO_2)}{d\theta} = k_5 K_9 (NO)^2 (O_2) \qquad (11\text{-}18)$$

As the temperature increases, the equilibrium constant K_9 decreases more rapidly than the rate constant k_5 increases, and so $d(NO_2)/d\theta$ decreases with respect to temperature.

Laidler† gives values for the rate constant in the expression

$$-\frac{d(NO)}{d\theta} = k_c (NO)^2 (O_2) \qquad (11\text{-}19)$$

They are tabulated in Table 11-1 as a function of temperature. It can be seen that k_c decreases as a function of temperature up to the region of 600°K.

TABLE 11-1. SPECIFIC REACTION-RATE-CONSTANT, TERMOLECULAR REACTION BETWEEN NO AND O_2†

T, °K	$k_c \times 10^{-3}$, liters^2/(mole^2)(sec)	T, °K	$k_c \times 10^{-3}$, liters^2/(mole^2)(sec)
80	41.8	413	4.0
143	20.2	564	2.8
228	10.1	613	2.8
300	7.1	662	2.9

† From K. J. Laidler, "Chemical Kinetics," McGraw-Hill Book Company, Inc., New York, 1950; with permission.

Wisconsin Process in the Manufacture of HNO₃

The manufacture of nitric acid starting with NH_3 continues to be the most economical process. There is, however, much interest in the so-called "Wisconsin process"‡ as a starting point. In that process, outlined schematically in Fig. 11-3, air at atmospheric pressure and 100°C is passed through a moving bed of ½-in. spheres of magnesium oxide. This bed preheats the air before it reaches the combustion zone. As a result of the preheating, a temperature of 2100°C is attained during combustion. At equilibrium, the gas at this temperature and atmospheric pressure would have about 2.4% NO, and equilibrium is essentially achieved. The gas leaves the combustion zone and passes

† K. J. Laidler, "Chemical Kinetics," p. 100, McGraw-Hill Book Company, Inc., New York, 1950.

‡ Farrington Daniels, Nitrogen Oxides and Development of Chemical Kinetics, *Chem. Eng. News*, **33**, 2370 (1955).

out through the second moving bed of pebbles that acts as a cooler. If the cooling is at a rate greater than 20,000°C/sec and is carried at least to 1500°C, only a small fraction of the nitric oxide formed at 2100°C will decompose. Therefore it is essentially in a state of "frozen equilibrium." Concentrations of 1.5 to 2.1% nitric oxide in an exit stream at 300°C have been obtained. The nitric oxide is catalytically oxidized on silica gel to NO_2, which is then adsorbed on the gel. It can later be

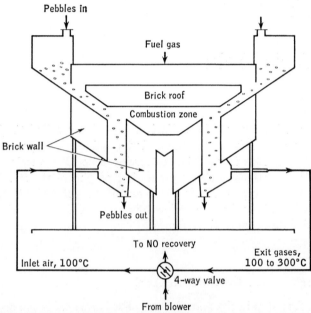

Fig. 11-3. Schematic diagram of Wisconsin process furnace for NO. (*From "Nitrogen Symposium: a Review of the Wisconsin Process for Nitrogen Fixation," Farrington Daniels, Chairman, November, 1955; with permission.*)

removed by heating to give a high concentration of NO_2 in the gas phase. Finally, the NO_2 can be absorbed in water to yield nitric acid in accordance with Eqs. (11-5) and (11-6).

Such a process was designed and operated by the Food Machinery and Chemical Corporation at Lawrence, Kans. The plant could produce 40 tons of HNO_3 per day and actually did manufacture a total of 2400 tons. Operation was suspended, however, because the process did not compete economically with the established process using ammonia. Future developments, however, may allow the Wisconsin process to be an important factor in the manufacture of HNO_3.

12

Sulfuric Acid

The production rate for sulfuric acid could be called the index for the economic health of the nation. It is the cheapest source of hydrogen ions in addition to having a specific role in many chemical reactions such as processing of phosphate fertilizers, petroleum, metals, etc. In the year 1953, a total of 15,530,000 tons of sulfuric acid computed as 100% acid was consumed in the United States, and that figure shows the magnitude of the industry.

Sulfur Sources for Sulfuric Acid

The first step in the manufacture of sulfuric acid is the production of SO_2. It is obtained by burning elemental sulfur, by roasting ores containing compounds such as FeS_2 and other metal sulfides, and by treating waste gases for the removal of sulfur-containing constituents such as H_2S and SO_2 itself. Of these sources the one of major economic interest is elemental sulfur produced by the Frasch process, and its cost is a controlling factor in the price of sulfuric acid. In parts of Louisiana and Texas, and in some other regions, large deposits of elemental sulfur exist several hundred feet below the earth's surface. Hot water under pressure is injected to melt the sulfur, which is then brought to the surface with compressed air as the lifting medium. The sulfur thus recovered is surprisingly pure and is the most desirable of the raw materials from the viewpoints of ease of handling, richness of the burner gases, and freedom from catalyst poisons. The other sources find use, however, on the basis of low cost under certain conditions.

The gases from a sulfur burner or an ore-roasting furnace contain SO_2 with excess O_2 and the unchanged N_2 from the air. These gases are subjected to one of two processes for producing sulfuric acid. The older process is the chamber process, and the other is the contact process. Even though the latter is superseding the former, it is possible that present and future developments could make the chamber process a continuing factor in the production of sulfuric acid. For that reason, a discussion of the chamber process as well as the contact process is in order.

The Chamber Process

The basic elements of the chamber process after the sulfur burner are the Glover tower, the chambers, and the Gay-Lussac towers; the process is shown schematically in Fig. 12-1. The burner is used to produce SO_2 by air oxidation of elemental sulfur or FeS_2. In the oxidation of sulfur, the reaction is given as

$$S(\text{rhombic}) + O_2(g) \rightarrow SO_2(g) \qquad \Delta H_{25°C} = -70,940 \text{ cal} \quad (12\text{-}1)$$

The gas containing about 8.5 to 9.0% oxygen, after addition of required makeup of NO from oxidation of NH_3, passes to the Glover tower which has the functions of

1. Cooling the burner gases from about 500 to about 100°C
2. Concentrating recirculated acid from the chambers, and at the same time supplying needed water vapor to the first chamber
3. Returning the catalyst, oxides of nitrogen, to the process after recovery in the Gay-Lussac towers

In the upper part of the Glover tower this reaction occurs:

$$2NOHSO_4(\text{aq}) + H_2O(l) \rightarrow H_2SO_4(\text{aq}) + NO(g) + NO_2(g)$$
$$(12\text{-}2)$$

The $NOHSO_4$ is called nitrous vitriol and is returned from the Gay-Lussac towers, and the water is furnished by the dilute recirculated acid. In addition to the reaction shown in Eq. (12-2), the following reaction also occurs in the upper part of the Glover tower:

$$2NOHSO_4(\text{aq}) + SO_2(g) + 2H_2O(l)$$
$$\rightarrow 2H_2SO_4 \cdot NO(\text{aq}) + H_2SO_4(\text{aq}) \quad (12\text{-}3)$$

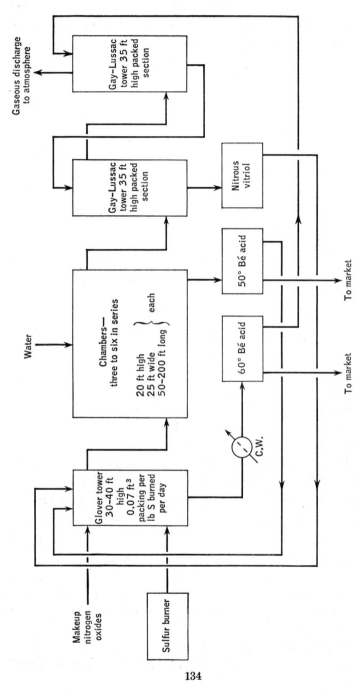

FIG. 12-1. Schematic diagram of chamber process for sulfuric acid. (*The Fluor Corporation, Ltd.*)

The $H_2SO_4 \cdot NO$ is called *violet acid,* and in the liquid phase it can decompose as follows:

$$H_2SO_4 \cdot NO(aq) \rightarrow H_2SO_4(aq) + NO(g) \qquad (12\text{-}4)$$

The SO_2, NO_2, NO, excess air, N_2, and water vapor pass at a temperature of 70 to 110°C from the top of the Glover tower into the first chamber. Sulfuric acid with a specific gravity corresponding to 60 degrees Baumé† (77.67 wt% H_2SO_4) is discharged from the bottom of the Glover tower.

Glover towers are square in cross-section with sides measuring 10 to 17 ft and heights of 30 to 40 ft. They are lead-sheathed, and the main structure is acid-proof brick. Internal packing assures intimate contact between the rising gases and the descending liquids. The gas velocity is about 0.8 ft/sec, and the tower volume corresponds to 0.07 ft³/lb of sulfur burned per day.

Upon entry into the chambers, the mixture of SO_2, O_2, and water vapor begins its reaction, catalyzed by oxides of nitrogen, to form sulfuric acid. The lead-lined chambers are each 50 to 200 ft long, 20 to 40 ft wide, and 20 to 30 ft high. The number of chambers in series ordinarily varies from three to six. Their purpose is to provide residence time for the reactants because, even with the gaseous catalyst, the reactions are slow. For chambers with moderate cooling, 7 ft³ of chamber space is required per pound of sulfur burned per day. The Mills-Packard chambers have water-cooled walls, and the space requirements drop to 2.75 ft³. A newer unit, the Kachkaroff-Guareschi design, claims 0.8 to 1 ft³ of chamber space per pound of sulfur per 24 hr. If development work continues to decrease the space requirements in the chamber process, it could again become competitive with respect to the contact process, especially when there is direct use for acid of intermediate concentration, as in manufacture of phosphate fertilizer.

Specifically the chambers perform the following functions in addition to giving residence time for the reactions:

1. Control temperature of reaction from entering value of about 100°C to final value of about 35°C by energy transfer to walls of chamber. The reactions are exothermic, and if the

---

† Degrees Baumé is a convenient means of expressing specific gravity in many circumstances. It is usually designated as °Bé, and for liquids heavier than water °Bé = 145 − 145/sp gr at 60°F referred to water at 60°F.

temperature were uncontrolled, unfavorable equilibria would result

2. Provide surfaces for condensation and collection of acid mist.

3. Provide entry of additional water into the process by way of steam or spray.

Taken over all, the chamber reactions are

$$2SO_2(g) + NO(g) + NO_2(g) + O_2(g) + H_2O(l)$$
$$\rightleftharpoons 2HSO_4NO(aq) \quad (12\text{-}5)$$
$$2HSO_4NO(aq) + H_2O(l) \rightleftharpoons 2H_2SO_4(aq) + NO(g) + NO_2(g)$$
$$(12\text{-}6)$$

In detail the reactions are

$$SO_2(g) + H_2O(l) \rightleftharpoons H_2SO_3(aq) \quad (12\text{-}7)$$
$$H_2SO_3(aq) + NO_2(g) \rightarrow H_2SO_4 \cdot NO(aq) \quad (12\text{-}8)$$
$$2(H_2SO_4 \cdot NO)(aq) + \tfrac{1}{2}O_2(g) \rightarrow 2HSO_4NO(aq) + H_2O(l)$$
$$(12\text{-}9)$$

or
$$2(H_2SO_4 \cdot NO)(aq) + NO_2(g) \rightarrow 2HSO_4NO(aq) + NO(g)$$
$$+ H_2O(l)$$
$$2HSO_4NO(aq) + SO_2(g) + 2H_2O(l) \rightleftharpoons 2H_2SO_4 \cdot NO(aq)$$
$$+ H_2SO_4(aq) \quad (12\text{-}10)$$
$$H_2SO_4 \cdot NO(aq) \rightleftharpoons H_2SO_4(aq) + NO(g)$$
$$(12\text{-}11)$$
$$2HSO_4NO(aq) + H_2O(l) \rightleftharpoons 2H_2SO_4(aq) + NO(g)$$
$$+ NO_2(g) \quad (12\text{-}12)$$
$$HSO_4NO(aq) + HNO_3(aq) \rightleftharpoons H_2SO_4(aq) + 2NO_2(g)$$
$$(12\text{-}13)$$

If there is insufficient water in the chambers, chamber crystals, HSO_4NO, form and catalyst is lost. Too much water gives dilute acid and allows formation of nitric acid from oxides of nitrogen. The nitric acid contaminates the sulfuric acid and represents a serious loss of catalyst gases. With proper operation of the chambers, 50°Bé (62.18%) acid is obtained. It is used mainly at the point of manufacture for converting phosphate rock to superphosphate fertilizer in accordance with the reaction

$$2[(CaF)Ca_4(PO_4)_3](s) + 7H_2SO_4(aq) + 3H_2O(l)$$
$$\rightarrow 3CaH_4(PO_4)_2 \cdot H_2O(s) + 2HF(g) + 7CaSO_4(s) \quad (12\text{-}14)$$

Some of the chamber acid is recirculated to the Glover tower for concentration. The 50°Bé acid cannot be shipped readily because it attacks steel, although more concentrated acid does not.

Discharge gases from the chambers pass to the Gay-Lussac towers. As mentioned, these towers are included in the plant design for the purpose of recovering oxides of nitrogen to be returned to the process by way of the Glover tower. Failure to recover and re-use these oxides would make the chamber process markedly uneconomical. Two Gay-Lussac towers, each the size of the Glover tower, are required to provide adequate surface area for the reactions. Finer packing is also used in order to give even more surface area per unit volume. In a standard design, the length of the packed section, with the two Gay-Lussac towers in series, is about 70 ft. If the packing has a void volume of about 50% and the superficial† gas velocity is about 0.6 ft/sec, the residence time of the gas is about 50 sec.

The gas and liquid in the Gay-Lussac towers flow counter-current to each other. Gas containing nitrogen, oxygen, water vapor, oxides of nitrogen, and a small quantity of SO_2 enters at about 35°C from the last chamber. Liquid in the form of 60°Bé (77.67%) acid at 40°C enters at the end of the Gay-Lussac system where spent gases are discharged. The oxides of nitrogen are recovered by the reverse of Eq. (12-12). A proper residual concentration of O_2 is required to give the balance between NO and NO_2 needed for that reaction. If too much SO_2 enters the Gay-Lussac system, oxides of nitrogen can be lost by the process which is described by the combination of Eq. (12-10) and (12-11) in that sequence. Because of the difficulty in maintaining optimum conditions, some oxides of nitrogen are always lost in the stack gases. Care must be exercised to minimize these losses because of the relatively high cost of oxides of nitrogen.

The Contact Process

The contact process for sulfuric acid is considerably less complicated than the chamber process. Because of the relative economy of operation and the direct production of a concentrated acid, the contact process has come to dominate the field of sulfuric acid manufacture.

† Superficial velocity is based on total internal cross section taken in the plane perpendicular to the gross flow.

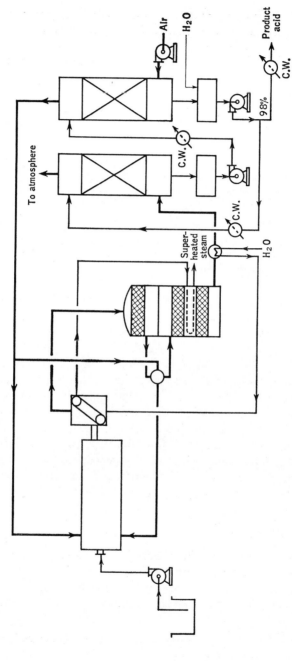

Molten sulfur charge tank   Furnace 16'∅ × 36'   Waste-heat boiler   3-stage converter 18'∅ × 32'   Economizer   SO₃ absorber 16'∅ × 36'   Air dryer 16'∅ × 35'

FIG. 12-2. Typical flow diagram of contact sulfuric acid process: 400 tons/day. (*The Fluor Corporation, Ltd.*)

The SO_2 for the reaction is readily obtained by burning sulfur in previously dried air in a rotary-type burner where molten sulfur is caused to drip through the input air stream. The same process can be used for SO_2 in making chamber acid, but, in the contact process shown schematically in Fig. 12-2, the air must be dry to minimize the reaction between H_2O and SO_3 in the converter. Also dust, chlorine, fluorine, arsenic, selenium, etc. must be avoided in order to prevent poisoning or damaging the catalyst used in the oxidation of SO_2 to SO_3. Dust can be removed by filtration or electrostatic precipitation after the gas has been cooled in the waste heat boiler to about 300°C after leaving the burner. The gas then passes into the converter.

Because of rate and equilibrium considerations, the usual practice in the conversion of SO_2 to SO_3 is to use more than one stage as shown in Fig. 12-2. The gases entering the first stage have an SO_2 content of about 7% with about 12% O_2 and 81% N_2. The reaction in the converters is

$$SO_2(g) + \tfrac{1}{2}O_2(g) \rightleftharpoons SO_3(g) \qquad \Delta H_{25°C} = -23,450 \text{ cal} \qquad (12\text{-}15)$$

Equilibrium data for the reaction are given in Table 12-1 from which Fig. 12-3 was prepared. At temperatures below about 500°C, the equilibrium lies far to the right. As the temperature is decreased, however, significant decreases in reaction rate occur. For example, the rate at 400°C is about one-fortieth of that at 500°C. In order to exploit the rate-equilibrium relationship, the practice of converting about 80% of the SO_2 in the first stage

TABLE 12-1. EQUILIBRIUM CONSTANTS† FOR THE REACTION
$$SO_2(g) + \tfrac{1}{2}O_2(g) \rightleftharpoons SO_3(g)$$

t, °C	K
400	468
500	52.5
600	9.74
700	2.55
800	0.859
900	0.348
1000	0.163

† Computed from the expression

$$\Delta F° = -22,600 + 21.36T$$

by G. N. Lewis and Merle Randall, "Thermodynamics and the Free Energy of Chemical Substances," p. 551, McGraw-Hill Book Company, Inc., New York, 1923; reproduced with permission.

of the converter is used. That stage is operated at about 550 to 575°C. Under these conditions the rate is high, and, although the equilibrium conversion is unfavorable, a large proportion of the conversion can be accomplished rapidly. The remainder of the SO₂ is converted at about 450°C to give about 95 to 97% of total conversion.

Catalysts for the contact process have received continuing interest. Platinum was given main attention until 1929. It is

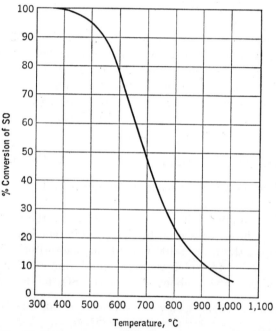

FIG. 12-3. Equilibrium conversion of SO₂ versus temperature for the reaction SO₂ + ½O₂ = SO₃ at a pressure of 1 atm and an initial gas composition of 7% SO₂, 13.9% O₂, and 79.1% N₂.

distributed on an inert carrier such as alumina, asbestos, MgSO₄, or silica gel with the last mentioned being most favored. The silica gel is impregnated with a solution of PtCl₄. That chloride is then reduced with hydrogen or SO₂ to give metallic platinum. A catalyst with about 0.1% platinum is used, and 2 to 4 troy ounces of the platinum are required per ton of H₂SO₄ made per 24 hr day. Today vanadium catalysts† made, for example,

† A. P. Thompson, Platinum vs. Vanadium Pentoxide as Catalysts for Sulfuric Acid Manufacture, *Trans. AIChE,* **27,** 264 (1931).

by mixing vanadyl sulfate and potassium vanadate with diatomaceous earth and activating by calcining are receiving major application. The initial cost of the platinum catalyst is greater, but a royalty is required for use of the vanadium catalyst, and it cannot be recovered after use. The costs are, therefore, about the same for the two catalysts. The lower limit for initiation of reaction with the platinum catalyst is 370°C and that for the vanadium catalyst is 400°C. On the other hand the vanadium catalyst is less easily poisoned by arsenic and associated compounds so that the vanadium catalyst deserves a slight preference.

Reaction Rate in the Contact Process

When more than one phase is involved, the rate expressions are ordinarily much more complex than for reactions in a single phase. The kinetics of the oxidation of SO_2 to SO_3 on a platinum catalyst as has been discussed by Uyehara and Watson[†] and by Hurt[‡] affords an example of such complexity. A combination of their work[§] gives a rate expression of the form

$$r = \frac{e^{-(8000/T)+14.154}}{(1 + \sqrt{p_{O_2}K_{O_2}} + p_{SO_3}K_{SO_3})^2} \left(p_{SO_2} \sqrt{p_{O_2}} - \frac{p_{SO_3}}{K} \right) \quad (12\text{-}16)$$

where r = reaction rate, lb moles of SO_2 oxidized/(hr)(lb of catalyst and carrier)

T = temperature at catalyst surface, °K

$p_{SO_2}, p_{O_2}, p_{SO_3}$ = partial pressures of SO_2, O_2, SO_3, respectively, in the gas phase at catalyst surface, atm

$K_{O_2} = e^{(20,360/RT)-(23.0/R)}$ = adsorption equilibrium constant for O_2 on given catalyst

$K_{SO_3} = e^{(16,800/RT)-(17.51/R)}$ = adsorption equilibrium constant for SO_3 on given catalyst

K = over-all gas-phase equilibrium constant

[†] O. A. Uyehara and K. M. Watson, Oxidation of Sulfur Dioxide, *Ind. Eng. Chem.*, **35**, 541 (1943).

[‡] D. M. Hurt, Gas-Solid Interface Reactions, *Ind. Eng. Chem.*, **35**, 522 (1943).

[§] O. A. Hougen and K. M. Watson, "Chemical Process Principles," part III, "Kinetics and Catalysis," p. 1021, John Wiley & Sons, Inc., New York, 1947.

Equation (12-16) results from the analysis of experimental data wherein it was found that the controlling reaction is one between SO_2 and an atom of oxygen on the surface of the catalyst. A combination of Eq. (12-16) with appropriate flow data would allow design of a catalytic converter for the oxidation of SO_2 to SO_3 in the presence of a platinum catalyst.

13

Sodium Hydroxide

Sodium hydroxide is an inexpensive source of hydroxyl ions and has tonnage use in the processing of rayon, aluminum, paper, soap, and petroleum. Its current annual rate of production is about 4 million tons, of which about 88% is made electrochemically and the remainder by the lime-soda process.

Electrochemical NaOH

In the electrochemical manufacture, an aqueous solution of NaCl is electrolyzed. Usually the solution is saturated with NaCl at the temperature of operation which is about 60°C. The over-all reaction for the process may be written as

$$NaCl(aq) + H_2O(l) \rightarrow \tfrac{1}{2}H_2(g) + \tfrac{1}{2}Cl_2(g) + NaOH(aq) \quad (13\text{-}1)$$

The main reactions occur, however, at the two electrodes. The desired cathode reaction is given by the relation

$$2H_2O + 2e \rightarrow H_2 + 2OH^- \quad (13\text{-}2)$$

That at the anode is

$$2Cl^- \rightarrow Cl_2 + 2e \quad (13\text{-}3)$$

If these were the only electrode reactions and all of the products from them were recovered, the current efficiency would be 100%. A number of factors serve to prevent attainment of this perfect performance, and some of them will be discussed. All positive ions will tend to migrate to the cathode and all negative ions to

143

the anode as indicated in Fig. 13-1.   Although Na^+ is present in much higher concentration than H^+, it migrates more slowly and has such a high deposition potential to overcome that it fails to deposit on the cathode, and so H^+ produces $H_2(g)$ instead. This leaves OH^- near the cathode, and the migration of Na^+ to that neighborhood leaves the solution there rich in the ions of NaOH.

The ions migrating toward the anode consist primarily of Cl^- and OH^-.   The latter ion has the greater mobility in the solution, but the major source near the cathode is farther away.   In

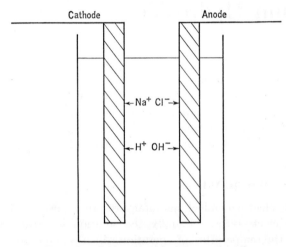

FIG. 13-1. Schematic chlorine-caustic cell.

accordance with Eq. (13-3), the desired result is to produce $Cl_2(g)$ at the anode, and therefore having OH^- reach the electrode is unfortunate for several reasons.   If OH^- discharges at the anode, it produces $O_2(g)$, which is an undesirable impurity in the valuable $Cl_2(g)$ produced, and represents wasted electrical energy as shown by the electrode reaction

$$2OH^- \rightarrow H_2O + \tfrac{1}{2}O_2 + 2e \qquad (13\text{-}4)$$

In addition, even if it does not discharge at the electrode, OH^- reacts with the Cl_2 with which the anode solution is saturated, in accordance with the reaction

$$\tfrac{1}{2}Cl_2 + OH^- \rightarrow HClO^- \qquad (13\text{-}5)$$

If this reaction is allowed to occur, it not only contaminates the solution but it also uses up two valuable products of the process. It is obvious, therefore, that steps should be taken to prevent OH^- from reaching the anode portion of the cell. This is ordinarily accomplished by maintaining a flow of brine through the cell so that the velocity of movement in the cathode solution away from the anode is greater than the migration velocity of OH^- toward the anode under the influence of the electric potential imposed on the cell. At the same time it is necessary to avoid having the flow movement carry Cl_2-saturated solution away from the immediate anode region mechanically and thus making possible the reaction of Eq. (13-5). The method by which these flow requirements are met will be illustrated in the discussion of various types of electrolytic cells in use. The necessity of circulating solution through the cell results in much of the NaCl content leaving the cell undecomposed. It is recovered, however, in a later step of the process and is recycled.

Hooker S Cell

The main type of production cell in use today is the Hooker S cell. It is of the submerged-diaphragm design, and a schematic cross section of the cell is shown in Fig. 13-2. Brine is fed to the anode side of a porous asbestos diaphragm placed between the electrodes, and flows from there into the cathode region. The transport of OH^- is then away from the anode. The diaphragm prevents convective mixing. It can be seen then that the opportunity for Cl_2 and OH^- to encounter each other and react according to Eq. (13-5) is essentially eliminated.

Vorce Cell

Another design to give maximum yield of OH^- is the Vorce cell shown schematically in Fig. 13-3. It is an unsubmerged-diaphragm cell. Brine is fed to the central anode chamber, passes out radially through the cathode diaphragm, and drips down the outside face of the perforated cathode to discharge at the bottom of the cell. Because of the brine flow from the anode side of the diaphragm to the cathode and the absence of accumulated cathode solution, the migration of OH^- to the anode zone is practically eliminated in this cell also.

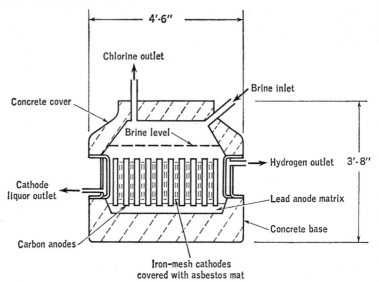

FIG. 13-2. Schematic sketch of a Hooker type S cell. (*Based on data from Hooker Electrochemical Company, Niagara Falls, N.Y., and from C. L. Mantell, "Industrial Electrochemistry," 3d ed., Table 63, p. 434, McGraw-Hill Book Company, Inc., New York, 1950.*)

Brine Purification

In both types of cells discussed above, purified brine must be used. Calcium, magnesium, and iron cannot be present because they would form insoluble hydroxides and block the flow in the cathode diaphragm. Also it is necessary to minimize the presence of $SO_4^=$ because of reduction in anode efficiency by the electrode reaction

$$2SO_4^= + 2H_2O \rightarrow 4H^+ + 2SO_4^= + O_2 + 4e \qquad (13\text{-}6)$$

As for the calcium, magnesium, and iron, removal is possible by pretreatment of the brine with Na_2CO_3 and $Ca(OH)_2$ to give $CaCO_3$, $Mg(OH)_2$, and $Fe(OH)_3$. Those compounds then can be removed as a sludge. In the case of the $SO_4^=$, removal of small quantities is possible with $BaCl_2$. Of main concern, however, is accumulation of $SO_4^=$ in the $NaCl(s)$ that is removed from the final NaOH solution and recirculated to the brine system. Here a wash of the NaCl to remove residual NaOH and Na_2SO_4 is an acceptable procedure.

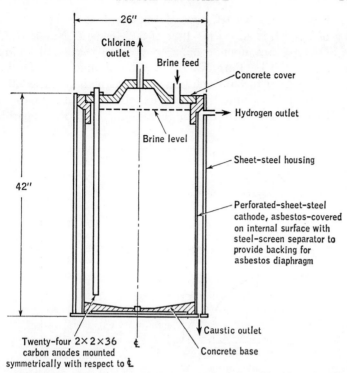

FIG. 13-3. Schematic diagram of Vorce caustic cell. (*Based on data from C. L. Mantell, "Industrial Electrochemistry," 3d ed., Fig. 135, p. 431, and Table 63, p. 436, McGraw-Hill Book Company, Inc., New York, 1950.*)

Concentration and Purification of NaOH Solutions

Liquor from the ordinary diaphragm cell contains 100 to 135 g per liter of NaOH and 130 to 170 g per liter of NaCl. The residual NaCl indicates that about 40 to 50% of the original charge of NaCl has been decomposed. In addition to the NaOH and NaCl, the brine will also contain residual impurities. It is then evaporated to recover salt and give commercial caustic.

Multiple-effect evaporators are used to concentrate the solution to 50% caustic. Nickel-clad evaporator shells are used along with nickel evaporator tubes in order to minimize contamination from iron and to prevent corrosion of the equipment. In the evaporation, NaCl crystallizes because its solubility in the 50% caustic is less than 1%. The NaCl is removed from the evaporators and returned to the brine make-up operation.

For very pure NaOH, several treatments may be used. If 50 g of Na_2SO_4 is added per liter of 50% caustic, $NaOH \cdot NaCl \cdot Na_2SO_4$ separates upon cooling to give only a small residual amount of NaCl. Pure NaOH may be obtained alternatively by cooling a 30 to 35% solution to yield solid hydrates of the type $NaOH \cdot 2H_2O$ and $NaOH \cdot 3\frac{1}{2}H_2O$, in accordance with Fig. 13-4. NaCl is left in the mother liquor, and the separated

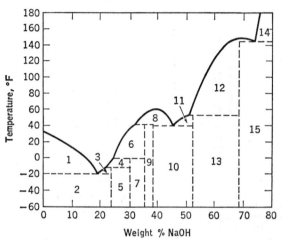

Weight % NaOH

FIG. 13-4. Hydrates in the $NaOH-H_2O$ system. 1. Ice + solution; 2. ice + $NaOH \cdot 7H_2O$; 3. $NaOH \cdot 7H_2O$ + solution; 4. $NaOH \cdot 5H_2O$ + solution; 5. $NaOH \cdot 7H_2O$ + $NaOH \cdot 5H_2O$; 6. $NaOH \cdot 4H_2O$ + solution; 7. $NaOH \cdot 5H_2O$ + $NaOH \cdot 4H_2O$; 8. $NaOH \cdot 3\frac{1}{2}H_2O$ + solution; 9. $NaOH \cdot 4H_2O$ + $NaOH \cdot 3\frac{1}{2}H_2O$; 10. $NaOH \cdot 3\frac{1}{2}H_2O$ + $NaOH \cdot 2H_2O$; 11. $NaOH \cdot 2H_2O$ + solution; 12. $NaOH \cdot H_2O$ + solution; 13. $NaOH \cdot 2H_2O$ + $NaOH \cdot H_2O$; 14. NaOH + solution; 15. $NaOH \cdot H_2O$ + NaOH. (*From Caustic Soda, Solvay Tech. Eng. Service Bull.* 6, 1954; *with permission.*)

hydrates are then melted and the pure solution concentrated. NaCl and $NaClO_3$ may be removed by countercurrent extraction of a 50% NaOH solution using a 70 to 90% solution of NH_3 in water which is immiscible with the 50% NaOH. The purification procedures give a caustic having less than 1% of impurities, whereas the standard grade of NaOH has impurities of about $2\frac{1}{2}$ to 3%.

The 50% solution can be evaporated in single-effect evaporators to about a 70% solution. Then that solution can be evaporated in a direct-fired cast iron pot to the anhydrous state by heating to 500°C. Any iron picked up from the pot or in previous processing can be removed by adding sulfur to the molten mass. Such an addition causes precipitation of ferrous sulfide. The melted NaOH at 350°C is then pumped from the pots to sheet-steel drums; it is solidified in these drums for shipment.

Mercury Cells

An improved procedure for producing pure NaOH without all the attendant processing described above is to use a mercury cell. Of special interest is the *de Nora cell* shown schematically

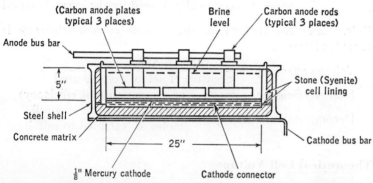

FIG. 13-5. Schematic cross section of 35-ft de Nora cell. [*From R. L. Kenyon and Patrizio Gallone, Chlorine and Caustic in Italy, Ind. Eng. Chem.,* **45**, 1162 (1953).

in Fig. 13-5. A flowing mercury cathode is used. A brine solution initially containing 310 g per liter of NaCl is electrolyzed. At the carbon anode $Cl_2(g)$ is given off, but at the mercury cathode, Na^+ is discharged to give a 0.05 to 0.15% amalgam with the mercury. In the dilute amalgam the activity of the sodium metal is so much less than when it is in the pure state that it can be deposited in preference to $H_2(g)$. Hydrogen is not formed because of the high overvoltage on the mercury cathode. The sodium is removed from the cell in the form of the amalgam, which goes to a decomposition tower packed with charcoal. Here the amalgam can be brought in at the top, and water at the bottom. As the two liquids move countercurrently, the sodium in the amalgam reacts with the water to give NaOH and hydrogen. By controlling the amount of water, pure NaOH solutions of various concentrations up to 75% can be produced.

Cell Efficiencies

In the operation of the electrolytic cells, a factor of major interest is the cost of the electrical energy. The energy requirement is studied in the light of the current efficiency, voltage efficiency, energy efficiency, and decomposition efficiency. They are defined as follows:

Current efficiency

$$= \frac{\text{amount of desired product recovered}}{\text{amount theoretically formed by the current passed}}$$

Unless otherwise designated, the cathode current efficiency is of major interest.

$$\text{Voltage efficiency} = \frac{\text{theoretical cell voltage}}{\text{negative of actual voltage used}}$$

$$\text{Energy efficiency} = (\text{voltage efficiency})(\text{current efficiency})$$

$$\text{Decomposition efficiency} = \frac{\text{moles of caustic leaving cell}}{\text{moles of NaCl fed to cell}}$$

Theoretical Cell Voltage

In an electrolytic cell, if the terminals were to be connected externally (for example, through an external resistance) there would be a tendency for the chemical reaction involved in the cell to take place in one direction or the other. This tendency represents a potential in the form of a voltage, which can be measured by means of a potentiometer circuit which allows only an exceedingly small current to flow. This voltage is called the *theoretical cell voltage*, and by common convention it is taken as positive in sign for a given cell reaction when the tendency is for the reaction to occur spontaneously in the direction indicated by the equation as written, i.e., to the right. In order to prevent the reaction from occurring when the external circuit is completed an external voltage of equal magnitude must be applied in the opposite direction. If an infinitesimally greater opposing voltage were to be applied, the reaction as written would be reversed, but at an infinitesimal rate. If the reverse reaction is to be carried on at a finite rate, a somewhat larger opposing voltage must be used, with a consequent lowering of voltage efficiency. It can be seen from this discussion that, if the cell reaction were to be rewritten in the opposite order, the sign of the theoretical cell voltage would be reversed. If in any given case the cell voltage is positive, the cell will act as a battery, but if the cell voltage is negative, energy must be invested in order to make the process operate as written.

Tabulations of individual electrode potentials are available in the literature, and theoretical cell voltages may be obtained from them by adding together the potentials for the two electrode reactions which will give the desired cell reaction. One must be sure that the convention as to signs used in the tabulation is understood. It should also be understood that the tabulated electrode potentials are usually for cases in which activities of all substances involved are unity and are called *standard electrode potentials*.

The theoretical cell voltage for the reaction

$$a\mathrm{A} + b\mathrm{B} + \cdots \rightarrow c\mathrm{C} + d\mathrm{D} + \cdots \tag{13-7}$$

can be calculated by use of the Nernst equation

$$\varepsilon = \varepsilon_0 - \frac{RT}{N\mathfrak{F}} \ln \frac{[\mathrm{C}]^c[\mathrm{D}]^d \cdots}{[\mathrm{A}]^a[\mathrm{B}]^b \cdots} \tag{13-8}$$

where ε = theoretical cell voltage
ε_0 = theoretical cell voltage when reactants and products are in state of unit activity
R = gas constant in appropriate units
T = absolute temperature
N = number of equivalents oxidized or reduced
$\mathfrak{F}$ = number of coulombs per faraday = 96,500
[A], etc. = activities of components in solution

Variation of Cell Voltage with Temperature

The change of the cell voltage with temperature can be obtained from the Gibbs-Helmholtz equation:

$$\frac{d\varepsilon}{dT} = \frac{\varepsilon}{T} + \frac{\Delta H}{N\mathfrak{F}T} \tag{13-9}$$

where ΔH = heat of reaction for the over-all reaction. A combination of Eqs. (13-8) and (13-9) would allow the theoretical cell voltage to be computed as a function of temperature.

Performance Characteristics of Caustic Cells

Table 13-1 gives a summary of the electrical characteristics and other additional data for each of the three cells that have

TABLE 13-1. PERFORMANCE CHARACTERISTICS OF VARIOUS CAUSTIC CELLS

	Hooker[a] S type	Vorce[a]	de Nora[b,c]
Voltage across cell	3.20–3.75	3.5–3.6	4.1–4.3
Current, amp	5000–10,000	950–1000	10,000–30,000
Current density, amp/in.^{2}			
Anode	0.32–0.64	0.14,[d] 0.34[e]	
Cathode	0.27–0.54	0.35,[d] 0.5[d]	1–3
Current efficiency, %	94–96	94–96	94–96
Energy efficiency, %	68–58.5	61–62	
Pounds NaOH per kwhr	0.96–0.83	0.86	0.77
Pounds Cl$_2$ per kwhr	0.86–0.74	0.79	0.67
Anode material	Graphite	Graphite	Graphite
Cathode material	Steel and wire screen	Perforated steel	Mercury
Raw material	Brine	Saturated brine	Saturated brine
Concentration of cathode NaOH, g/liter	135–138	90–105	
Salt concentration, discharge brine	14–15%	16%	270 g/liter
Effluent temperature, °C	85	65	70

[a] C. L. Mantell, "Industrial Electrochemistry," 3d ed., Table 63, p. 433, McGraw-Hill Book Company, Inc., New York, 1950; with permission.

[b] Anon., Acres of de Nora Cells, *Chem. Eng.*, **59**, part 2, 146, (August, 1952).

[c] Richard L. Kenyon and Patrizio Gallone, Chlorine and Caustic in Italy, *Ind. Eng. Chem.*, **45**, 1162 (1953).

[d] Based on entire anode or cathode surface.

[e] Based on active anode or cathode surface.

been discussed. Generally speaking there is little difference in electrical performance, and the main differences are in mechanical design and product purity. The fact that the energy efficiencies are as low as 58 to 68% results from the resistance offered to passage of current through the electrolyte. Extra voltage beyond that required for the electrode reactions must be applied to overcome this resistance, thus increasing the actual voltage above the theoretical requirement and lowering the voltage efficiency. The cell resistance is influenced by the specific conductivity of the electrolyte and by the distance between the electrodes.

Chemical Production of NaOH

Caustic soda can be made chemically as well as electrolytically. Today about 12% of the caustic is made chemically, and the equation for the reaction is

$$Ca(OH)_2(s) + Na_2CO_3(aq) \rightleftharpoons 2NaOH(aq) + CaCO_3(s) \quad (13\text{-}10)$$

The process is conducted at a temperature of 80 to 95°C to intensify the rate of reaction and rate of particle growth in order

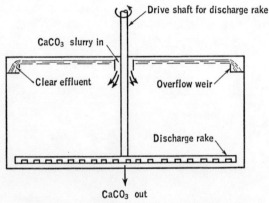

FIG. 13-6. Thickener tank for CaCO₃ slurry.

to increase the rate of settling of CaCO₃. The precipitated CaCO₃ is separated from the solution in thickeners of the type shown schematically in Fig. 13-6. Also in the region of temperature cited, no compounds such as Na₂CO₃·CaCO₃·5H₂O are formed.

The equilibrium expression for Eq. (13-10) is written as

$$K = \frac{K_1}{K_2} = \frac{[Ca^{++}][OH^-]^2}{[Ca^{++}][CO_3^=]} = \frac{[OH^-]^2}{[CO_3^=]}$$

As the activity of $CO_3^=$ decreases, the per cent of conversion increases. In the chemical manufacture of caustic, solutions containing 10 to 12% NaOH are obtained. They have the advantage over the electrolytic cell liquors of the absence of the excess NaCl which is found in the latter solutions. This makes the dilute chemical caustic solutions usable directly in cases that do not require high concentrations of NaOH.

Problems

1. *a.* The heat of fusion of lead nitrate is 88.5 cal/g. What is the corresponding value in Btu/lb?

b. The heat capacity of liquid ammonia at constant pressure and at a temperature of 100°C is 1.45 cal/(g)(°C). What are the corresponding values of temperature and heat capacity in English units?

c. The heat of combustion of acetylene (C_2H_2) is 306,100 cal/g mole. What is the corresponding value in Btu/lb mole? In Btu/lb?

d. The standard value of gravitational acceleration is 980.7 cm/sec². What is the corresponding value in ft/sec²? What is the weight in pounds (English force-length-time system) of a mass of 1 kg when located where a standard value of g prevails? What would be the weight when $g = 971$ cm/sec²?

e. If a constant force of 10 lb is used to move a body at a constant velocity of 1.5 ft/sec until the body has traveled 10 ft, what are the total energy and the power involved?

2. A metal tank has the shape of a right circular cone with apex at the bottom. It is 6 ft high, and at the top has a diameter of 30 in. It is filled with a solution which varies in concentration from top to bottom. The distribution is such that the specific weight (i.e., weight per volume) is given by the expression, $\sigma = 63.0 + 0.830h$, in which h is the distance below the top of the tank in feet, and the specific weight σ is in lb/ft³. What is the weight of the solution in the tank? The inside dimensions given for the tank may be taken as exact, and so they do not limit the precision of the result.

3. A steel tube of constant diameter and 10 ft long is filled with crystals of a water-soluble solid having progressively varying size of particle. Water enters at one end and flows steadily through the tube. At the water-entrance end, the solid offers an exposed surface of 3000 ft² per ft³ of tube volume. The exposed surface S, in ft²/ft³, decreases

155

along the length x of the tube, in feet, measured from the entrance end, in accordance with the equation, $-dS/dx = 52x + 10$. As the water progresses, it dissolves some of the solid material, and this solution process can be characterized by the fact that the rate of change of the concentration c, expressed in pounds of solute per 100 lb of water, with respect to distance x, is proportional, at any position along the tube, to the exposed surface S there, and also to the difference between the saturation concentration for the solute and the concentration existing at the point in question. At the temperature existing, the saturation concentration C_s for this solute is 35 lb per 100 lb of water. From a small side tube located 3 ft from the entrance end of the main tube, a sample of liquid is withdrawn, and it shows a concentration of 10 g of solute per 100 g of water.

What concentration would you expect to find in the solution leaving the end of the tube? If the constants for equations used above were to remain unchanged, what initial value of exposed surface S_0 would be necessary in order that the concentration of solute at the outlet end of the tube be 30 lb per 100 lb of water?

4. A piston is fitted in a cylinder so that it can move along the horizontal axis of the cylinder. Against the left-hand face of the piston a variable force acts, its numerical magnitude being given by the relation $\underline{F}_L = 500/(10 - l)$ where l is the distance in inches from a given initial position, and $\underline{F}$ is the force in pounds. Against the right-hand face of the piston another force acts, which is given, in the same units, by $\underline{F}_R = 180 - 3.0l^2$. A force of 10 lb is required to move the piston in either direction against frictional resistance alone. The distance l is positive in sign when measured to the left of the initial position.

a. How much energy, in foot-pounds, is required from the action of additional forces to move the piston 6 in. to the left from the position in which $l = 0$?

b. To move the piston 6 in. to the right from the position in which $l = 0$?

c. What positive value of l gives the smallest force (numerically) that will just hold the piston in balance when it is moving toward the left?

5. Work from the following facts: 453.6 g = 1 lb, 2.54 cm = 1 in., a temperature interval of 1°C = 1.8°F, density of mercury = 13.6 g/cc, standard boiling point of water is at 100°C or 212°F.

a. The "ice point" is the temperature at which solid ice is in equilibrium with liquid water saturated with air at 1 atm pressure, and is at 0°C, or 273.16°K (degrees Kelvin, or centigrade absolute). What are the values for this point on the Fahrenheit (°F) and Rankine (°R, or °F abs) scales? What value on the Rankine scale corresponds to 0°F?

b. At a pressure of 1 atm abs and a temperature corresponding to the ice point, the volume occupied by a gram-molecular weight of a perfect gas is 22,400 cc. What is the volume in cubic feet occupied by a pound-molecular weight under the same conditions? What is the temperature in degrees Fahrenheit and the pressure in pounds per square inch absolute (psia)?

c. A mercury manometer is connected to a tank filled with gas. The other arm of the manometer is open to the air. A barometer in the room shows a reading of 758 mm. The mercury meniscus in the open arm of the manometer is 6.5 cm higher in level than that in the other arm. What are the "gauge pressure" (that corresponding to the manometer reading; in other words, the excess above atmosphere pressure in the room) and the "absolute pressure" (the actual pressure in the tank) in psi?

d. If the tank in part *c* is filled with nitrogen gas and it is 4 ft in diameter by 10 ft long, the temperature being 70°F, what is the weight of gas in the tank in pounds?

e. With the conditions the same as given above except that the temperature is 100°F and the gas is hydrogen instead of nitrogen, how many lb moles (pound-molecular weights) of gas would be present in the tank?

6. *a.* If 1 lb mole of a perfect gas has a volume of 359 ft³ at a pressure of 14.70 psia and a temperature of 32°F, what is the value of the universal gas constant in (psi)(ft³/mole)/°R? What is the specific gas constant *b* in (psi)(ft³/lb)/°R for nitrogen? What is the universal gas constant in Btu/(lb mole)(°R)?

b. A large closed tank contained nitrogen gas at 70°F and 14.70 psia. A small high-pressure cylinder of nitrogen was weighed; its contents were discharged into the larger tank; and the small cylinder was again weighed. The decrease in weight of the cylinder was found to be 5.45 lb. The temperature in the large tank remained at 70°F, and the final pressure was found to be 17.47 psia. What was the volume of the tank? Under the conditions existing, nitrogen behaves very much like a perfect gas.

c. At the end of the operation carried out in part *b*, it is desired to connect another high-pressure cylinder to the tank, allowing the pressures in the cylinder and the tank to equalize by flow of the nitrogen gas between them, the temperature at the end of this process still being 70°F. The volume of the cylinder in this case is 1.00 ft³, and the volume of the connecting tubing is negligible. What weight, in pounds, of nitrogen gas should be in the cylinder when it is ready to connect to the tank if the final pressure in the whole system is to be 19.00 psia? What is the pressure in the small cylinder before connecting to the tank?

Work in English units throughout.

7. Moist air at 80°F enters a cooler in which part of the moisture is being condensed and drained off as a liquid, the partially dried air then being reheated to 70°F. The total pressure in all parts of the apparatus is 14.64 psia. The partial pressure of water vapor in the incoming air is 0.46 psi, whereas that in the outgoing air is 0.12 psi.   Under these conditions, both air and water vapor can be taken as perfect gases, with molecular weights equal to 29.0 and 18.0, respectively.

For each 1000 ft³ of moist air entering the system, how many pounds of liquid water is withdrawn, what volume of air (including its remaining water vapor) leaves the system, and what weight of dry air enters the system?   What are the values of the absolute humidity of the entering air and the outgoing air in pounds of moisture per pound of dry air?

8. In the evaporator unit shown in the accompanying figure, 5 tons of a salt brine per hour containing 12% NaCl and 5% KCl is being concentrated.   The temperature in the whole unit is 212°F.   The concentrated liquor being drawn off is almost up to saturation concentration for KCl.   The crystal mass being removed contains 70% solids. At 212°F a solution which is saturated with both salts contains 21.6% KCl and 16.9% NaCl.   Assume for present purposes that a deficiency of either salt in a solution does not affect the ratio of the other salt to water in a saturated solution.   All percentages are by weight.

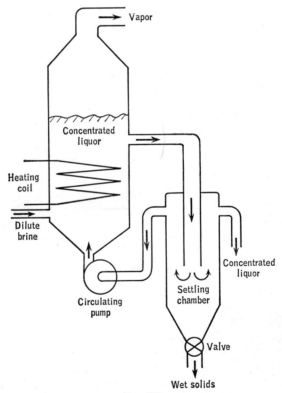

Fig. P8.

Determine material balances for KCl, NaCl, and water, showing the amount of each material in each entering and departing stream on the basis of 1 hr of operation.

If the concentrated liquor stream withdrawn is cooled to 77°F, how much solid will be formed and what will be its percentage composition? At 77°F a saturated solution contains 11.2% KCl and 20.4% NaCl.

9. NH_3 is oxidized to NO in the converter section of a nitric acid plant operating at 100 psig. The feed to the converter is 8% NH_3, and the remainder is air. In the converter, 94% of the NH_3 is converted to NO. The remainder is converted to N_2 and H_2O. If 98% of the originally formed NO is absorbed in the absorber to give HNO_3, and the remaining 2% is discharged from the absorber as NO, what is the analysis of the gas discharging from the absorber expressed on a dry basis?

10. A brine contains 16.9% NaCl and 12.7% Na_2CO_3 in solution in water. When the brine is carbonated (treated with CO_2 gas), $NaHCO_3$ precipitates and is filtered off. The filtrate consists of 18.9% NaCl, 2.3% Na_2CO_3, and 2.1% $NaHCO_3$, and the remainder is water. The precipitate leaving the filter contains 95% solid $NaHCO_3$ and 5% solution wetting the solid particles. The moist precipitate is then heated in a rotary kiln to convert the $NaHCO_3$ to Na_2CO_3. All percentages given are by weight.

Per ton of incoming brine processed, neglecting dissolved but unreacted CO_2:

a. How much moist precipitate is recovered?

b. How much filtrate is produced?

c. How much solid Na_2CO_3 is produced if all $NaHCO_3$ is decomposed in the rotary kiln?

d. How much CO_2 has gone into combination in the carbonation step?

e. How much CO_2 is released in the rotary kiln?

f. What is the percentage of impurity in the solid product?

g. What percentage of the incoming Na_2CO_3 is recovered as solid product?

11. Sea water has a solids content of 3.7% and a specific gravity of 3.5°Bé.† It is made up of the following, reported as per cent of total solids:

NaCl	77.76
$MgCl_2$	10.88
$MgSO_4$	4.74
$CaSO_4$	3.60
K_2SO_4	2.46
$CaCO_3$	0.34
$MgBr_2$	0.22

† $°Bé = 145 - \dfrac{145}{\text{sp gr } (60°F/60°F)}$ for liquids heavier than water.

In the manufacture of NaCl by solar evaporation the brine is first pumped into an evaporation pond where evaporation proceeds until essentially all of the $CaCO_3$ is precipitated, as is the $CaSO_4$. The brine is then pumped to a crystallizing pond where NaCl with slight impurities of $MgSO_4$, $MgCl_2$, and NaBr is crystallized. The brine at the end of crystallization is at 30°Bé and a concentration of 523 g per liter of solution, and 91.3% of the NaCl has been crystallized. Calculate the pounds of water evaporated to give 10,000 tons of salt per season. Take the loss of $MgSO_4$, $MgCl_2$, and $MgBr_2$ in the NaCl as negligible.

From the following evaporation data determine the acres of crystallizing ponds required to give the 10,000 tons of salt in one season:

Month	Rainfall, in.	Evaporation, in.
April	1.36	3.38
May	1.14	5.31
June	0.67	6.62
July	0.00	7.81
August	0.00	7.81
September	0.00	4.94
October	0.77	2.94

Assume that evaporation rates for ponds are average rates associated with salt solutions at different concentrations through the season.

12. What would be the flue-gas analyses in the following cases?

a. Pure carbon burned to completion with the stoichiometric amount of air?

b. Ethyl alcohol (95% C_2H_5OH and 5% water) completely burned using 10.0% excess air?

c. Acetylene (C_2H_2) completely burned using a mixture consisting of 1 volume of pure oxygen to 1 volume of dry air, furnishing 5.8% excess oxygen beyond that stoichiometrically required?

d. Hexane (C_6H_{14}) burned in the stoichiometric amount of air for complete combustion, but, although all the hydrogen is oxidized, the dry flue gas contains 0.91% CO.

For each case state the number of moles of water vapor resulting from the combustion per mole of dry flue gas produced.

13. A boiler furnace is being fired with a natural gas whose analysis is as follows: 83.6% CH_4, 9.7% C_2H_6, 4.8% C_3H_8, 1.5% C_4H_{10}, and 0.4% N_2. An analysis of the flue gas shows it to contain 3.1% O_2 and no CO, the remainder being presumably CO_2 and N_2.

a. What are the percentages of CO_2 and N_2 in the flue-gas analysis?

b. What percentage of the air stoichiometrically required for combustion is the excess air used?

c. How many pounds of water vapor will be present with each cubic foot of dry flue gas (measured at 400°F and 14.5 psia) if both the natural gas and the air used for combustion are saturated with water vapor at 60°F, the barometer reading 755 mm Hg? The vapor pressure of water at 60°F is 13.3 mm Hg.

14. In a certain boiler furnace, powdered coal is used as fuel. The results of analysis of the coal show 68.8% C, 5.0% H, 17.6% O, 1.5% N, and 7.1% ash (all by weight on dried sample); 22.6% moisture in coal sample as fired. It is found that the solid material suspended in or dropped out of the exit gases contains 7.9% C and 92.1% ash. The air used amounts to the stoichiometric requirement for complete combustion of all combustible matter plus 5.0% of this amount in excess, and under those conditions 0.9% of the total combined carbon in the exit gases passes out as CO while the rest leaves as CO_2.

  a. What percentage of the total carbon of the coal is lost in the exit solid material?

  b. What is the exit gas analysis?

  c. What weight of water vapor accompanies each cubic foot of dry flue gas (550°F and 1 atm pressure)?

15. A solid material containing 15% moisture is being dried to a moisture content of 2%, both percentages by weight on a wet basis. The stock temperature during drying is 150°F, and the heat of vaporization of water at this temperature is 1008.2 Btu per lb of water evaporated. The specific heat of the completely dry stock is 0.26 Btu/(lb)(°F), that of dry air is 0.24 Btu/(lb)(°F), and that of water vapor is 0.45 Btu/(lb)(°F). Both moist stock and entering make-up air enter the dryer at 70°F. The air leaving the dryer is at 100°F and contains 3% moisture by weight on a moist basis.

A diagrammatic flow sheet of the dryer system is shown below. Part of the air leaving the dryer is recycled through the heater in order to supply the energy necessary for the drying. Part of the air is discarded

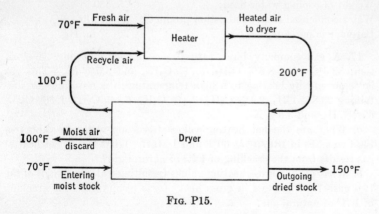

FIG. P15.

in order to carry moisture from the system, and make-up air is taken into the system to replace it.   The entire system is at 1 atm pressure.

Assuming that the moisture content of the entering air is negligible, and that thermal losses from the walls of the system can be neglected, calculate on the basis of 1 hr of operation, when 1 ton of incoming moist stock per hour is being processed, each of the following quantities:

    a. Weight of outgoing stock produced
    b. Weight of water evaporated
    c. Weight of moist air discarded
    d. Weight of fresh dry air entering
    e. Weight of air recycled: (1) dry air only, and (2) moist air
    f. Btu of energy added in the heater

16. Calculate the net and gross calorific values of a sample of fuel gas which gave the following results in a steady-flow gas calorimeter. The calorific value of a fuel is equal to $-\Delta H_{70°F}$ for its combustion. The net value is for the resulting water (if the fuel contains hydrogen) as a gas, and the gross value is with the water ending as liquid.   In such a calorimeter, gas admixed with air is burned in a bunsen burner at atmospheric pressure, and the temperature of the products is brought back close to room temperature by flowing cooling water in a jacket. After the apparatus had come to a steady state, the readings were taken over a measured time interval as follows:

Time interval of the run:	2 min, 50 sec
Metered volume of gas burned (saturated):	0.111 ft³
Wet-meter temperature:	70.0°F
Gauge pressure in meter:	0.28 in. Hg
Intake cooling water temperature:	65.13°F
Outlet cooling water temperature:	78.02°F
Weight of cooling water used:	8.550 lb
Water condensed from combustion products:	0.010 lb
Barometric pressure:	29.52 in. Hg

17. A gas company buys natural gas of the following composition: 82.3% CH_4, 8.5% C_2H_6, 3.7% C_3H_8, and 5.5% N_2.   This gas is "cracked" by heating to a high temperature, the resulting gas containing 23.8% CH_4, 2.4% C_2H_6, 2.3% C_2H_2, 6.3% C_2H_4, 1.4% C_3H_6, 60.2% H_2, and 3.6% N_2.

    a. What are the net heating values (resulting water as vapor) of the two gases in Btu/ft³ at 60°F and 1 atm?   What loss of net heat of gas results from the cracking of 1 ft³ of natural gas?

    b. What are the gross heating values (resulting water as liquid) of the two gases?   What loss in gross heat of gas results from the cracking of 1 ft³ of natural gas?

c. What product other than gas results from the cracking? What quantity is produced?

Use the following molal heats of combustion (water as vapor) in Btu/ mole:

CH_4	346,000
C_2H_6	611,000
C_3H_8	876,000
C_2H_2	543,000
C_2H_4	584,000
C_3H_6	836,000
H_2	104,000

$$H_2O(g) \rightarrow H_2O(l) \qquad \Delta H_{60°F} = -18,970 \text{ Btu}$$

18. A gaseous mixture in the proportion of 3 moles of hydrogen to 1.2 moles of nitrogen is fed at 860°F and 6000 psia to a catalyst chamber operating under those conditions. On the basis of the stipulations listed below, determine the composition of the gas leaving the converter in mole per cent, and the amount of cooling water needed in lb/hr.

a. Ammonia is to be produced at the rate of 800 lb/hr.

b. Cooling water required to keep the converter at 860°F enters at 80°F and leaves at 120°F.

c. The reaction is $\frac{1}{2}N_2 + \frac{3}{2}H_2 = NH_3$, $\Delta H = -21,600$ Btu, under the conditions prevailing in the converter.

d. The catalyst is effective in bringing the gas mixture to equilibrium before it leaves the converter.

e. The equilibrium constant for the reaction written above at the prevailing pressure is considered to be the following function of temperature when T is in degrees Rankine and K is expressed in terms of partial pressures of the components in the reacting mixture in atmospheres:

$$\log_{10} K_P = \frac{5045}{T} - 6.012$$

f. Dalton's law applies; i.e., in the gas mixture the partial pressure of each component is proportional to its mole fraction.

19. For the reaction

$$CO_2(g) + C(s) = 2CO(g)$$

taking place at 70°F and 1 atm absolute pressure, $\Delta H = +73,800$ Btu per mole of CO_2. What would be the enthalpy change

a. When 10 lb of carbon reacted with CO_2 in accordance with this equation at 1 atm and 1000°F?

b. When 1000 ft³ of CO, as measured at standard conditions (a pressure of 1 atm and 32°F, the temperature of the ice point), is produced at 1 atm and 1000°F?

The molal heat capacities at constant pressure for these substances may be taken as follows:

For $CO_2(g)$: $C_P = 7.70 + 2.94 \times 10^{-3}T - 2.56 \times 10^{-6}T^2$
For $C(s)$: $C_P = 2.673 + 1.452 \times 10^{-3}T + 0.036 \times 10^{-6}T^2$
For $CO(g)$: $C_P = 6.76 + 0.337 \times 10^{-3}T + 0.040 \times 10^{-6}T^2$

in which T is in degrees Rankine, and C_P is in Btu/(mole)(°R).

20. A mixture of CO and O_2 containing 40% CO is conducted through an insulated tube in a steady-state process at 14.7 psia. The gas mixture enters at a temperature of 1600°F and leaves at 1800°F. What is the fractional conversion of CO when there is no energy transfer to or from the wall of the reactor? The following information may be used:

Compound	Heat of formation at 25°C, cal/g mole	Molal heat capacity at constant pressure T, °K
CO	−26,394	$6.76 + 0.606 \times 10^{-3}T + 0.13 \times 10^{-6}T^2$
O_2	0	$6.76 + 0.606 \times 10^{-3}T + 0.13 \times 10^{-6}T^2$
CO_2	−94,030	$7.70 + 5.3 \times 10^{-3}T - 0.83 \times 10^{-6}T^2$

21. For the reaction,

$$SO_2(g) + \tfrac{1}{2}O_2(g) \rightleftharpoons SO_3(g)$$

$$\Delta F^\circ_{298°K} = -16,900 \frac{cal}{\text{mole of } SO_2} \quad \text{and}$$

$$\Delta H^\circ_{298°K} = -23,450 \frac{cal}{\text{mole of } SO_2}$$

The following expressions may be taken as describing the heat capacities of the gases, when C_P is in cal/(mole)(°K), and T is in degrees Kelvin.

For SO_3: $C_P = 6.077 + 23.54 \times 10^{-3}T - 9.69 \times 10^{-6}T^2$
For SO_2: $C_P = 7.70 + 5.3 \times 10^{-3}T - 0.83 \times 10^{-6}T^2$
For O_2: $C_P = 6.76 + 0.606 \times 10^{-3}T + 0.13 \times 10^{-6}T^2$

Using these data, determine the gas composition which would be attained when a mixture originally consisting of 13% SO_2, 8% O_2, and 79% N_2 is brought to equilibrium at 600°C and 1 atm, the nitrogen gas remaining inert. Qualitatively, what effect upon composition would you expect if *a.* The pressure were to be increased above 1 atm, but the temperature was kept the same?

b. The temperature were to be increased above 600°C but the pressure was kept the same?

22. A gas mixture consisting of 14% SO_2, 7% O_2, and 79% N_2 continuously enters a reaction chamber at 700°F and leaves at 1000°F. If the chamber walls are insulated so that there is no thermal transfer to the surroundings, what will be the composition of the outgoing gas stream, assuming that N_2 gas is unreactive and that the following data apply:†

$$SO_2(g) + \tfrac{1}{2}O_2(g) \rightleftharpoons SO_3(g) \qquad \Delta H^\circ_{700°F} = -42{,}210 \text{ Btu per mole of } SO_2$$

For SO_3: $C_P = 6.077 + 10.42 \times 10^{-3}T$
For SO_2: $C_P = 6.147 + 6.03 \times 10^{-3}T$
For O_2: $C_P = 6.095 + 1.31 \times 10^{-3}T$
For N_2: $C_P = 6.524 + 0.694 \times 10^{-3}T$

in which C_P is in Btu/(mole)(°R) and T is in degrees Rankine.

23. Reduction of metallic oxides by means of carbon is one of the common methods for recovery of metals. This procedure has been used for reducing magnesia to magnesium. The reaction is carried out at 2100°C and 1 atm and is given as follows:

$$MgO + C \rightleftharpoons Mg + CO$$

Assuming that, at the temperatures involved, thermodynamic equilibrium is rapidly achieved, above what temperature should the walls of the reaction vessel be maintained to prevent formation of C and MgO on the walls as a result of the reversal of the above reaction?

The following information is available:

$$K = (P_{Mg})(P_{CO}) = 21.1 \qquad \text{at } 2100°C$$

where pressures are in atmospheres;

$$\Delta H \text{ for reaction} = 142.6 \text{ kcal at } 2100°C$$

Molal heat capacities in cal/(mole)(°K) as a function of T in degrees Kelvin:

For MgO: $C_P = 10.86 + 1.197 \times 10^{-3}T - 2.087 \times 10^5 T^{-2}$
For C: $C_P = 2.673 + 2.617 \times 10^{-3}T + 0.1169 \times 10^6 T^2$
For CO: $C_P = 6.76 + 0.606 \times 10^{-3}T + 0.13 \times 10^{-6}T^2$
For Mg (vapor): $C_P = 4.9$

24. SO_2 may be readily oxidized by O_2 in the presence of a catalyst to give SO_3. A mixture having the following composition in volume

† The equations for C_P are simplified in order to reduce the time required for calculation in this problem, and so they are not suitable for other use.

per cent

SO$_2$	7.5
O$_2$	13.5
N$_2$	79.0

is reacted at 850°F and 19 psia. If it is assumed that thermodynamic equilibrium is achieved, what is the composition of the gas system after reaction? For the reaction

$$SO_2 + \tfrac{1}{2}O_2 = SO_3$$

the following data† are available:

T, °K	$\Delta F°/T$, cal/°K
801	−6.84
852	−5.21
900	−3.73
953	−2.33
1000	−1.22

25. Ammonia will decompose at moderate temperatures in accordance with the following reaction:

$$2NH_3 \rightleftharpoons N_2 + 3H_2$$

For this reaction, as written, the following data may be used:

t, °F	$\Delta F°/T$, Btu/(mole NH$_3$)(°R)
644	−6.86
716	−8.11
788	−9.23
860	−10.23
932	−11.15

Ammonia gas enters a chamber where equilibrium is attained at 740°F and 16 psia. If it may be assumed that the gases present follow ideal-gas behavior under existing conditions, what would be the composition of the equilibrium mixture in terms of volume per cent?

26. Steam at atmospheric pressure is to be passed through a bed of hot carbon under such conditions that equilibrium will be established. What will be the minimum temperature that can be maintained without having more than 2.0 mole % CO$_2$ in the moist equilibrium gas? What will be the analysis of the equilibrium gas on a dry basis? The following reactions occur:

$$H_2O(g) + C(s) \rightarrow CO(g) + H_2(g) \tag{1}$$
$$CO(g) + H_2O(g) \rightarrow CO_2(g) + H_2(g) \tag{2}$$

† D. M. Yost and H. Russell, Jr., "Systematic Inorganic Chemistry," p. 314, Prentice-Hall, Inc., Englewood Cliffs, N.J., 1944.

The equilibrium constants for these reactions may be taken as

t, °F	$(K_p)_1$	$(K_p)_2$
980	0.46	4.05
1340	2.71	1.38
1500	10.30	0.97
1550	15.00	0.89
1600	21.09	0.82
1700	41.21	0.72
1800	75.34	0.64

27. Methane and steam are to be reacted catalytically at atmospheric pressure. The initial mixture contains 1 mole of methane for every 3 moles of steam. If the space velocity is such that thermodynamic equilibrium is achieved, what is the lowest operating temperature that will assure at least 99.5% conversion of the methane?

The following reactions occur:

$$CH_4 + H_2O \rightleftharpoons CO + 3H_2 \tag{1}$$
$$CO + H_2O \rightleftharpoons CO_2 + H_2 \tag{2}$$

Use the following equilibrium constants for the respective reactions:

t, °F	K_1	K_2
980	0.033	4.05
1340	27.3	1.38
1500	260	0.97
1550	450	0.89
1600	870	0.82
1700	2640	0.72
1800	4710	0.61

28. For the reaction

$$H_2(g) \rightarrow 2H(g)$$

the free-energy change expressed in calories per gram mole of initial hydrogen at T °K is given by the expression†

$$\Delta F° = 81{,}000 - 3.5T \ln T + 0.00045T^2 + 1.17T$$

What is the per cent dissociation at 4000°R and a pressure of 14.7 psia?

† G. N. Lewis, and Merle Randall, "Thermodynamics and the Free Energy of Chemical Substances," p. 471, McGraw-Hill Book Company, Inc., New York, 1923.

Also what is the heat of reaction in Btu/lb mole under those conditions? What commercial application is suggested for the use of that information?

29. Using the data given below, calculate the theoretical composition (wet basis) of water gas at 1000°C, being produced at 1 atm pressure, the following equilibria being established:

$$H_2O(g) + C(s) \rightleftharpoons CO(g) + H_2(g)$$
$$C(s) + CO_2(g) \rightleftharpoons 2CO(g)$$

What will be the heating value of this gas in calories per liter (volume measured at 1 atm and 0°C) and in Btu/ft³ (volume measured at 1 atm and 60°F)

a. With water condensed?

b. With water as vapor?

What would be the flue-gas analysis (dry basis) for this gas completely burned with the stoichiometric amount of dry air?

EQUILIBRIUM RELATIONSHIPS OVER CARBON
(Pressure in atmospheres)

Temperature of carbon, °C	p_{CO_2}/p^2_{CO}, atm^{-1}	$p_{H_2O}/(p_{CO})(p_{H_2})$, atm^{-1}
700	1.37	0.769
800	0.189	0.165
900	0.0357	0.0446
1000	0.00855	0.0143
1100	0.00246	0.00524
1200	0.000824	0.00213
1400	0.000129	0.000449

$$H_2(g) + \tfrac{1}{2}O_2(g) \rightarrow H_2O(l) \quad \Delta H_{15.6°C} = -68,300 \text{ cal}$$
$$CO(g) + \tfrac{1}{2}O_2(g) \rightarrow CO_2(g) \quad \Delta H_{15.6°C} = -67,700 \text{ cal}$$
$$H_2O(g) \rightarrow H_2O(l) \quad \Delta H_{15.6°C} = -10,600 \text{ cal}$$
$$\Delta H_{0°C} = -10,735 \text{ cal}$$

30. SO₂ is to be oxidized to SO₃ by a catalytic conversion, using platinum as a surface coating on ⅛-in. cylindrical alumina pellets. The entering gas stream contains 7.0% SO₂, 13.9% O₂, and 79.1% N₂. The temperature of the reactor is kept at 860°F, and the feed enters at that temperature. The reactor contains 3130 lb of catalyst. The entering gas is fed at the rate of 1000 lb moles/hr.

What will be the composition of the outlet gas stream from this reactor?

What will be the SO₃ output of this reactor in pounds per 24 hr?

Use the following rate data for the conditions obtaining in this case:

| | Rate, lb moles of SO_2 |
% conversion	converted/(hr)(lb of catalyst)
0	0.146
10	0.1000
20	0.0674
30	0.04667
40	0.0319
50	0.0215
60	0.0148

31. SO_2 is to be oxidized to SO_3 in a catalytic converter containing platinum as a surface coating on $\frac{1}{8}$-in. cylindrical alumina pellets. Compare the size of a converter operating at 420°C to give 90% conversion of the SO_2 in a gas system containing 6.5% SO_2 and 93.5% dry air where the weight rate of flow is 350 lb/(hr)(ft²), with two converters in series operating under the same conditions except for conversion and temperature. In the series operation, the first converter operates at 500°C for 70% of the conversion and the second converter at 420°C for the remaining 20%. The following rate data are available† for the given conditions:

RATE DATA

[In g moles of SO_2 converted/(hr)(g of catalyst)]

t, °C	% conversion						
	0	10	20	30	40	50	60
350	0.011	0.0080	0.0049	0.0031	—	—	—
360	0.0175	0.0121	0.00788	0.00471	0.00276	0.00181	—
380	0.0325	0.0214	0.01433	0.00942	0.00607	0.00410	—
400	0.0570	0.0355	0.02397	0.01631	0.0110	0.00749	0.00488
420	0.0830	0.0518	0.0344	0.02368	0.0163	0.0110	0.00745
440	0.1080	0.0752	0.0514	0.03516	0.0236	0.0159	0.0102
460	0.146	0.1000	0.0674	0.04667	0.0319	0.0215	0.0138
480	—	0.1278	0.0898	0.0642	0.0440	0.0279	0.0189
500	—	0.167	0.122	0.0895	0.0632	0.0394	0.0263

32. Hydrochloric acid catalyzes the liquid-phase esterification reaction between acetic acid and ethyl alcohol.‡ The reaction is reversible

† J. M. Smith, "Chemical Engineering Kinetics," p. 342, McGraw-Hill Book Company, Inc., New York, 1956.

‡ J. M. Smith, "Chemical Engineering Kinetics," p. 85, McGraw-Hill Book Company, Inc., New York, 1956.

and may be written as

$$CH_3COOH + C_2H_5OH \rightleftharpoons CH_3COOC_2H_5 + H_2O$$

Determine the fractional conversion of the acetic acid after 100 min at 212°F when the initial aqueous solution has a volume of 150 gal in which there are 310 lb of acetic acid, 625 lb of ethyl alcohol, and 50 lb of HCl. The specific weight of the solution may be taken as 8.6 lb/gal and assumed to have a constant value throughout the course of the reaction. Assume that no material is vaporized during the reaction period.

The rate equation for the disappearance of acetic acid may be written as

$$\mathbf{r} = -\frac{dC_{\text{acetic acid}}}{d\theta} = k_c C_{\text{acetic acid}} C_{\text{ethyl alcohol}} - k_c' C_{\text{ester}} C_{H_2O}$$

where for the reaction conditions given above

$$k_c = (4.8 \times 10^{-4})(\text{liter})/(\text{g mole})(\text{min})$$
$$k_c' = (1.6 \times 10^{-4})(\text{liter})/(\text{g mole})(\text{min})$$

What is the fractional conversion of acetic acid when chemical equilibrium is achieved?

33. Ethyl acetate in aqueous solution hydrolizes slowly, but if hydrochloric acid is added it catalyzes the hydrolysis. The reaction is reversible and is expressed by the equation,

$$CH_3COOC_2H_5 + H_2O \rightleftharpoons CH_3COOH + C_2H_5OH$$

The rate equation for the disappearance of the ester is

$$\mathbf{r} = -\frac{dC_{\text{ester}}}{d\theta} = k_c C_{\text{ester}} C_{\text{water}} - k_c' C_{\text{acid}} C_{\text{alcohol}}$$

A batch consisting of 1 ton of ester solution containing 713 lb of ester and 78 lb of HCl is allowed to stand at a temperature of 194°F for 1 hr. Under these conditions the following values of reaction rate constants may be used:

$$k_c = 0.148 \text{ ft}^3/(\text{lb mole})(\text{hr})$$
$$k_c' = 0.455 \text{ ft}^3/(\text{lb mole})(\text{hr})$$

The specific weight of the solution may be taken as 64.3 lb/ft³, which may be assumed to be constant throughout the process. Assume that no vaporization occurs, that the solution is homogeneous, and that the temperature remains constant.

What weights of the various constituents are present in the batch at the end of the hour? What weights would be present if sufficient time were to be allowed for the batch to reach an equilibrium state?

34. Methane is passed through a heated tube. It is decomposed to give hydrogen and solid carbon according to the reaction

$$CH_4 \rightarrow 2H_2 + C$$

The tube has an inside diameter of 1 in. and a length of 36 in. It is maintained at a temperature of 2100°F, and the process may be considered as occurring isothermally at that temperature. The pressure is 14.7 psia, and 0.15 lb of CH_4 is fed to the tube per hour. Determine the fractional conversion of CH_4 for one pass through the tube.

The decomposition of CH_4 into C and H_2 may be taken as irreversible and first-order with respect to CH_4. The rate equation may be taken as

$$\mathbf{r} = -\frac{dC_{CH_4}}{d\theta} = k_c C_{CH_4}$$

and the rate constant at 2304°R as 0.06 sec^{-1}, and at 2423°R as 0.26 sec^{-1}.

Assume perfect gases and that any carbon formed settles immediately on the reactor wall without changing the inside diameter of the channel.

35. Ethane gas decomposes at high temperature to give ethylene and hydrogen according to the equation

$$C_2H_6(g) \rightarrow C_2H_4(g) + H_2(g)$$

The rate of disappearance of ethane at any particular time is equal to a rate constant multiplied by the concentration of ethane present at that time. At 1023°F, take the first-order rate constant for this irreversible reaction as 2.8×10^{-5} sec^{-1}, and that at 1225°F as 7.4×10^{-3} sec^{-1}.

What would be the partial pressure of ethylene if a container with a volume of 1 ft^3 originally filled with ethane at 1 atm pressure and 1150°F, were kept at that temperature for 10 min? Ideal-gas relations may be assumed.

36. One pound of nitrogen gas per hour containing a small concentration of hydrogen peroxide is to be passed through a heated pyrex glass tube in order to decompose the peroxide. The total pressure throughout the tube is 1 atm and the partial pressure of H_2O_2 in the incoming gas is 2mm Hg. The tube has an inside diameter of 1 in. and a length of 9 ft. The temperature during passage through the tube is uniformly 930°F. The reaction occurring is

$$H_2O_2(g) \rightarrow H_2(g) + O_2(g)$$

It is essentially irreversible and may be taken as first order with respect to H_2O_2. Under the conditions stated, the rate equation is

$$-\frac{dC_{H_2O_2}}{d\theta} = k_c C_{H_2O_2}$$

in which k_c may be taken as 30.0 min^{-1}. The gases involved may be taken as ideal under the prevailing conditions, and, as a reasonable approximation, it may be assumed that the total number of moles does not change appreciably. What will be the partial pressure of H_2O_2 in the gas leaving the tube? How long would the tube have to be in order to decompose 99% of the H_2O_2?

37. A 5.0 N solution of monoethanolamine in water is to be used to recover CO_2 from a flue gas in a steady-state operation. Subsequently the solution will be stripped by boiling at atmospheric pressure to recover the CO_2 for use in making liquid CO_2.

The flue gas has the following percentage composition:

CO_2	12.4
CO	1.2
O_2	5.4
N_2	81.0

If the plant is to recover 500 lb of CO_2 per hour, and 90% of the CO_2 absorbed from the flue gas is recovered, how many gallons of 5.0 N monoethanolamine per hour must be circulated with absorption at 70°F? Assume that the stripper leaves 0.012 lb of CO_2 per gal for each per cent of monoethanolamine, and that equilibrium is achieved in the absorption process.

EQUILIBRIUM DATA FOR 5.0 N MONOETHANOLAMINE SOLUTION IN WATER

Partial pressure CO_2, mm	Liquid concentration, moles CO_2/ mole amine	Partial pressure CO_2, mm	Liquid concentration, moles CO_2/ mole amine	Partial pressure CO_2, mm	Liquid concentration, moles CO_2/ mole amine
0°C:		25°C:		50°C:	
751.5	0.761	742.9	0.657	677.0	0.574
272.2	0.679	254.9	0.601	245.3	0.527
206.2	0.649	98.7	0.563	71.9	0.525
80.1	0.600	44.6	0.539	71.5	0.505
79.4	0.610	10.6	0.507	10.4	0.453
11.5	0.600				

At 25°C the density of the 5.0 N monoethanolamine solution is 1.002 g/cc.

38. A plant uses a mixture of hydrogen and nitrogen, consisting of 3 moles of H_2 for each mole of N_2, to produce 20 tons per 24-hr day of ammonia. The continuous-flow reactor with catalyst is operated at a pressure of 100 atm and a temperature of 450°C, with an exit space velocity of 15,000 hr⁻¹. The ammonia produced in the reactor is separated from the exit gases by condensation, and the remaining gas is recycled to be mixed with make-up gas and fed back to the reactor. What is the reactor volume for this operation? How many moles of hydrogen and nitrogen gas, respectively, will be recycled from the reactor exit per hour of operation? How many Btu of energy must be transferred away from the reactor each hour in order to maintain its temperature at 450°C? Can you suggest a use for this energy in connection with the process?

Molal heat capacities of the gases may be expressed by the following equations:

For H_2: $C_P = 6.85 + 1.56 \times 10^{-4}T + 6.79 \times 10^{-8}T^2$
For N_2: $C_P = 6.76 + 3.37 \times 10^{-4}T + 4.02 \times 10^{-8}T^2$
For NH_3: $C_P = 6.70 + 3.50 \times 10^{-3}T$

in which C_P is in Btu/(mole)(°R) and T is in degrees Rankine.

39. In carrying out one of the nitrogen fixation processes, air is heated to a high temperature with attainment of equilibrium in the formation of NO from the elements. In order to preserve the NO formed in this way, it is necessary to cool the gas mixture very rapidly so as to prevent as much decomposition of NO as is feasible. In a given case the air at atmospheric pressure is to be heated to 4600°F and then cooled rapidly to 3000°F without having more than 20% of the NO decomposed during the cooling. What cooling rate would be necessary on the assumptions that the cooling rate is constant and that during the cooling process no N_2 and O_2 combine to form NO? The fixation reaction is

$$O_2 + N_2 \rightleftharpoons 2NO$$

Use a standard free-energy change which is the following function of temperature:

$$\Delta F_T^\circ = 77,800 - 5.00T$$

in which ΔF_T° is in Btu per mole of O_2, and T is in degrees Rankine.

The decomposition during cooling is in accordance with the reverse reaction expressed above, and the rate equation for it may be taken as

$$-\frac{d(NO)}{d\theta} = k_c(NO)^2$$

The quantity k_c in ft^3/(mole)(sec) is the following function of temperature:

$$k_c = 2.63 \times 10^{12} e^{-125,000/RT}$$

in which T is in degrees Rankine, R is in Btu/(mole)(°R), and k_c is in ft^3/(mole)(sec).

40. A plant is to make 10 tons of NH_3 per day, using a feed stream where the mole ratio of N_2 to H_2 is 1:3. The reactor is to be operated at a temperature of 450°C and a pressure of 100 atm. What volume of catalyst would you use? Explain. If all the gas discharged after condensation of NH_3 is recycled, give the number of moles of N_2 and

H_2, respectively, in the recycle stream per hour. How many Btu per hour are transferred from the reactor?

Molal heat capacities in cal/(g mole) (°K) and T in degrees Kelvin are

For H_2: $C_P = 6.85 + 2.8 \times 10^{-4}T + 2.2 \times 10^{-7}T^2$
For N_2: $C_P = 6.76 + 6.06 \times 10^{-4}T + 1.3 \times 10^{-7}T^2$
For NH_3: $C_P = 6.70 + 6.3 \times 10^{-3}T$

41. Water gas and producer gas are used as sources of nitrogen and hydrogen in the synthesis of ammonia. Analyses are given as follows:

Component	Water gas, %	Producer gas, %
CO_2	4.9	5.0
CO	42.1	26.8
H_2	51.8	5.4
N_2	1.2	62.8

A 2:1 volume ratio of water gas to producer gas is catalytically reacted with water vapor to convert all the CO to CO_2. The system is then processed to remove CO_2, and the mixture of nitrogen and hydrogen is passed on to the converter where ammonia synthesis occurs. Assuming that equilibrium conditions are achieved in the converter operating at 150 atm and 480°C, determine the percentage of ammonia in the exit mixture, using the following equilibrium data obtained for stoichiometric proportions:

Temperature, °C	Pressure, atm	NH₃ content of gases, vol %
420	100	21.5
460	100	14.9
500	100	10.4
540	100	7.4
580	100	5.4
620	100	4.0
500	40	4.8
500	140	13.6
500	180	16.4
500	240	20.1

42. a. In a platinum-gauze ammonia oxidation unit, the gases reaching the gauze are at 1200°F and contain 8.3% NH_3, no decomposition having occurred. Assuming a 93% conversion to NO, no formation of N_2, and no loss of thermal energy, what would be the temperature of the gases leaving the catalyst? The heat of reaction may be considered to be independent of temperature and equal to 95,000 Btu per lb mole of NH_3 converted, the resulting water being gaseous.

b. The gas leaving the oxidation unit is cooled and absorbed in water, 95% of the oxidized nitrogen in the gas being thus recovered, and the rest lost as NO in the exit gas. The unoxidized NH_3 is decomposed to N_2 and H_2O during the cooling process. What is the analysis of the gas leaving the absorption system?

Heat capacities of gases in Btu/(mole)(°R), as a function of Rankine temperature T are as follows:

For O_2, N_2, or NO: $C_P = 6.76 + 0.337 \times 10^{-3}T + 0.040 \times 10^{-6}T^2$
For NH_3: $C_P = 6.70 + 3.5 \times 10^{-3}T$
For H_2O: $C_P = 8.22 + 0.083 \times 10^{-3}T + 0.413 \times 10^{-6}T^2$

43. A rotary sulfur burner receives an initial or primary air supply (at the sulfur intake point) which has a total pressure of 748 mm Hg, and contains water vapor with a partial pressure of 10 mm Hg. The gas leaving the rotary chamber contains only SO_2, N_2, S_4, and water vapor. It has a total pressure of 748 mm Hg and a partial pressure of S_4 of 65 mm Hg.

a. For each mole of primary moist air, how many moles of moist air must be added as a secondary supply before the gas enters the stationary combustion chamber, in order to burn the gaseous sulfur to SO_2 and produce an outgoing gas which carries enough O_2 to convert the SO_2 present to SO_3?

b. How much secondary air is needed to burn the sulfur to SO_2 and produce an outgoing gas which contains 11.2% SO_2 when considered on a dry basis?

44. Iron pyrites, FeS_2, are being roasted to give SO_2 for manufacture of sulfuric acid by the chamber process. The pyrites ore moves countercurrent to the air stream. In one day, 20 tons of ore are burned. It contains 84% FeS_2, 1.5% H_2O, and 14.5% inorganic gangue that is inert. The discharge gas from the burner contains 8% SO_2, 10.6% O_2, and 81.4% N_2. The air enters at 77°F and 50% relative humidity. Likewise the ore enters at 77°F. If the cinder leaving the burner contains no residual sulfur and is at a temperature of 750°F, and the gas stream leaves at 800°F, what is the energy loss per hour from the walls of the roaster? The following data may be used:

Mean heat capacities of gases at 14.7 psia between 77 and 800°F in Btu/(mole)(°F):

N_2	7.11
O_2	7.45
H_2O	8.36
SO_2	10.95

Heats of formation at 77°F in Btu/mole:

SO_2	$-127,800$
Fe_2O_3	$-357,000$
O_2	0
FeS_2	$-69,600$

Mean heat capacity of cinder between 77 and 750°F = 0.18 Btu/ (lb)(°F)

Pounds of H_2O per pound of air at 77°F and 50% relative humidity = 0.01

Heat of vaporization of water at 77°F = 1050.4 Btu/lb

45. A rotary sulfur burner uses refined sulfur and air. The burner gases containing 8.0% SO_2 go directly to a contact converter operating at a pressure of 14.7 psia and a temperature of 1060°F. The gases then enter a second converter operating at a pressure of 14.7 psia and a temperature of 840°F. What percentage of the SO_2 entering each chamber is converted to SO_3, and what is the over-all percentage conversion of SO_2 to SO_3?

46. In a lead-chamber sulfuric acid plant, a test was made on the Glover tower, and during the test period the following streams of materials entered the tower:

Gas entering at the bottom containing 1.44 lb moles of SO_2, 1.70 moles of O_2, 13.81 moles of N_2, and 0.29 mole of H_2O

Chamber acid fed to the top, consisting of 63 wt % H_2SO_4 and 37 wt % H_2O

Nitric acid fed to the top, consisting of 36 wt % HNO_3 and 64 wt % H_2O, to make up losses from the system

580 lb of Gay-Lussac acid fed to top, consisting of 77.0 wt % H_2SO_4, 22.1 wt % H_2O, and 0.885 wt % N_2O_3

During the test, operating conditions remained steady and the concentrated acid leaving the base of the tower contained 78.0 wt % H_2SO_4. The gas stream leaving the top of the tower contained, on a *wet basis*, 6.44% SO_2, 8.75% O_2, 74.59% N_2, 0.770% NO, and 9.45% H_2O.

The SO_2 lost from the system amounted to 1.52×10^{-3} moles per mole of N_2 leaving the Gay-Lussac tower.

Determine:

    a. The percentage of the incoming SO_2 converted to H_2SO_4 in the Glover tower

    b. The loss in pounds of fixed (or combined) nitrogen per 1000 lb of H_2SO_4 (basis of 100% acid) produced by the plant

    c. The weight of nitric acid fed to the tower

    d. The weight of acid leaving the bottom of the tower

    e. The weight of chamber acid fed to the top of the tower

47. A contact sulfuric acid plant produces 98.5% acid by dissolving SO_3 in 97% acid in an absorption tower. In another tower 20% oleum is produced by dissolving SO_3 in 15% oleum. In order to keep the plant operating on a continuous basis, part of the 98.5% acid is diluted with water to make 97% acid for feed to the first tower. Another part of the 98.5% acid is used to dilute a suitable amount of 20% oleum to give the 15% oleum needed for feed to the oleum tower. The rest of the 98.5% acid produced is withdrawn as product. If this plant produces for market 25 tons of 20% oleum and 80 tons of 98.5% acid per day of continuous operation, how much feed goes to each of the towers, and what are the requirements of water and SO_3 per day?

48. The feed to a Hooker S cell is 37.3 lb of NaCl per hour in an aqueous solution. Discharge from the cathode liquor analyzes as 130 g of NaCl and 135 g of NaOH per 1000 g of water. The cell operates at 5100 amp and 3.4 volts. What are the current efficiency and the production of NaOH expressed in lb/kwhr? If the current efficiency is the same at both electrodes, what is the production of Cl_2 in lb/kwhr?

49. A de Nora cell is being used to manufacture high-purity NaOH for use in viscose rayon manufacture. A purified saturated solution of NaCl at 60°C is fed at a rate of 170 gph (gal/hr) to the cell operating at the same temperature. The solution is 27.0 wt % and has a specific gravity of 1.187 (60°C/4°C). Depleted brine at a concentration of NaCl of 20 wt % is discharged from the cell.

The anode and cathode current efficiencies are 95.2%. The theoretical cell voltage is -2.22 volts, and the voltage efficiency is 51.1%. Calculate the following:

a. Pounds of NaOH produced per kilowatthour of energy used
b. Pounds of Cl_2 produced per kilowatthour of energy used
c. Volume of H_2 at 60°F and 14.7 psia produced per day

If for the electrode

$$Na(0.2\% \text{ Na in Hg}) \rightarrow Na^+(\text{sat. soln. of NaCl}) + e^-$$

the equilibrium potential is 1.82 volts, and that for the electrode reaction

$$\tfrac{1}{2}H_2(1 \text{ atm}) \rightarrow H^+(\text{pH 9}) + e^-$$

is approximately 0.6 volt, why can Na^+ be discharged to form an amalgam in mercury without formation of hydrogen gas? The condition of pH 9 would approximate the pH in the saturated solution of sodium chloride in the cell.

50. A plant electrolyzing sodium chloride brine supplies 8 tons of chlorine per 24-hr day to an adjacent paper mill for bleaching pulp. In the same period the plant also produces sufficient chlorine to fill 60 cylinders, each containing 100 lb of liquid chlorine, and 5 drums, each containing 1 ton of liquid chlorine. The type of cell in use required 3.7 volts to operate at a 5000-amp rate, and at this rate gives current efficiencies of 95% for chlorine and for hydroxide ion. The liquor leaving the cells contains 17.2 g of NaCl and 11.1 g of NaOH in 100 g of solution. It may be assumed that the lowering of current efficiency is due to the reaction

$$Cl_2 + 2OH^- \rightarrow Cl^- + ClO^- + H_2O$$

and that the ClO^- remains undecomposed when the liquor leaves the cell although it decomposes to Cl^- during analysis and during the commercial evaporation of the liquor.

a. What volume of chlorine gas (60°F and 14.8 psia) must be handled per hour?

b. What would be the total amperage required at the cells if all the cells were to be operated in parallel?

c. How many cells would be required, if an allowance of three cells out of service is made to care for maintenance and repairs? How would you suggest arranging the electrical hookup of these cells to give reasonable generator loading? What voltage and amperage would be required from generator equipment?

d. What is the power requirement of this plant, assuming that 6% of the total energy input is lost in transformers, generators, and busbar systems? What is the daily energy cost if paid for at the rate of 0.35 cent/kwhr? What is the energy cost per pound of chlorine marketed?

e. How many cylinders could be filled with hydrogen if each contained 200 ft³ of gas measured at 60°F and 14.8 psia?

f. What are the voltage and energy efficiencies of these cells?

g. What fraction of the chloride fed to the cells is recovered in the form of chlorine? How much salt is fed to the cells per day? How much caustic soda is recovered per day on evaporation of the liquor?

51. 22°Bé hydrochloric acid (35.8% HCl) is being manufactured at the rate of 10 tons per 24-hr day by burning chlorine gas continuously in an atmosphere of hydrogen gas, cooling the gases, absorbing in water, and collecting the excess hydrogen for re-use. If the recycled hydrogen is 10% of the total hydrogen entering the reaction chamber and contains no Cl_2 or HCl, and if the gases are fed to the burners at 150°F, how much heat must be dissipated per hour from the system in order

a. To bring the gases to a temperature of 150°F before absorption? and

b. To keep the absorption system at constant temperature during absorption?

c. With the proportions given, what is the maximum temperature that might be reached in the combustion chamber?

Use the following values:

For HCl gas: $C_P = 6.50 + 0.00056T$ Btu/(mole)(°R) when $T = $ °R
For H$_2$ gas: $C_P = 6.50 + 0.00050T$

$$\tfrac{1}{2}H_2 + \tfrac{1}{2}Cl_2 \rightarrow HCl \qquad \Delta H_{150°F} = -39,600 \text{ Btu}$$
$$HCl(g) + nH_2O(l) \rightarrow HCl(aq) \qquad \Delta H = -25,500 \text{ Btu}$$
$$\text{under conditions given}$$

52. Na$_2$CO$_3$ may be causticized with lime to give NaOH in the lime-soda process for caustic.† Derive an expression for the per cent conversion of Na$_2$CO$_3$ to NaOH in terms of the initial concentration of Na$_2$CO$_3$ and the solubility products of Ca(OH)$_2$, and CaCO$_3$. What is the limiting conversion as the concentration of the initial Na$_2$CO$_3$ approaches zero? If the enthalpy change for the causticizing reaction may be taken as zero, what is the per cent conversion of Na$_2$CO$_3$ to NaOH at 90°C where at 16°C

$$K_1 = (Ca^{++})(OH^-)^2 = 3.98 \times 10^{-5}$$
$$K_2 = (Ca^{++})(CO_3^=) = 9.85 \times 10^{-9}$$

with the concentrations expressed in moles/liter, and the initial concentration of Na$_2$CO$_3$ is 1.2 moles/liter for the temperature of operation? Assume that sufficient lime is present to insure a solid phase of slaked lime at all times.

† W. K. Lewis, A. H. Radasch, and H. C. Lewis, "Industrial Stoichiometry," 2d ed., p. 290, McGraw-Hill Book Company, Inc., New York, 1954.

Index

181